Revision for
SCIENCE
Key Stage 4
• with answers •
REVISED NATIONAL CURRICULUM EDITION

Revision for
SCIENCE
Key Stage 4
• with answers •

REVISED NATIONAL CURRICULUM EDITION

JOE BOYD   WALTER WHITELAW

JOHN MURRAY

© Joe Boyd and Walter Whitelaw 1994, 1997

First published in 1994
by John Murray (Publishers) Ltd
50 Albemarle Street
London W1X 4BD

Reprinted 1994, 1995, 1996
Second edition 1997

Layouts by Eric Drewery.
Cartoons by Richard Duszczak.
Line illustrations by Art Construction and Mike Humphries.

Typeset in 11/12 pt New Century Schoolbook by Wearset, Boldon, Tyne and Wear.
Printed and bound in Great Britain by St Edmundsbury Press, Bury St Edmunds.

A CIP catalogue record for this book is available from the British Library.

ISBN 0 7195 7422 6

Contents

Introduction

During the last few years, you have gained a great deal of important knowledge and understanding from the National Curriculum for Science. You have probably forgotten some of the work. This work must be revised and relearned for your examinations. Unfortunately, revision is hard work and it is easy to avoid. Some of the most common ways are shown in the cartoons below.

a) Working in the wrong place

b) Pretending

c) Worrying too much

d) Not worrying enough

e) ..... or getting bored

f) Putting too much effort into socialising

First, get organised!

Plan

It is always a good idea to plan your revision. The plan below is an example of a revision timetable. Each box represents 2 or 3 hours of work. There is one box for a school day, and two for weekend and holiday days. Make up something like this for your own revision, and stick it on your wall.

Study/Revision planner

1 Plan all your revision before you begin it.
2 Each box represents 2 or 3 hours of work.
3 Try to keep to your plan, but don't be afraid to change it.

	Mon	Tues	Wed	Thurs	Fri	Sat am	Sat pm	Sun am	Sun pm
	Sc2 Foundation	Sc2 Foundation	Sc2 Foundation	Look up words in bold	20 March	Sc2 Higher	Sc2 Higher	Day off	Day off
	Look up words in bold	Sc3 Foundation	Sc3 Foundation	etc	27 March				
					3 April				
					10 April				

Be an active learner

Try to be an active learner. Rather than just reading through notes, make sure that you write or draw or underline as you read through them. Make summaries and answer questions. Use spider diagrams and revision summaries (examples of these are given below).

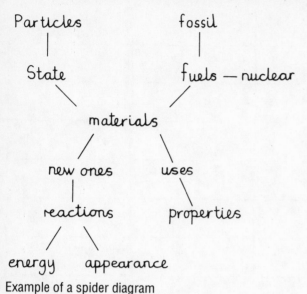

Example of a spider diagram

Fossil fuels — millions of years

Coal
oil
natural gas

dead organisms
crushed
changed

Combustion — join with O_2
exothermic

Example of a revision summary

Next, use this book!

Get your own copy

This book contains the main ideas of the whole Science course, Key Stage 4. Your teacher will suggest which level you should aim for. Learn the levels in order, from Foundation upwards. If you are aiming for Higher level make sure you have studied all the Foundation level first.

Write all over it

1 Each section starts by listing the main 'big' ideas. Read these and make sure you understand the sense of the work. The paragraph letters link with each big idea.
2 Read one paragraph and underline the key phrases.
3 Continue with the other paragraphs. Complete any diagrams when asked.
4 At the end of each double page, read over your work. Tick the boxes when you know and understand the work.
5 Check your answers at the back of the book. (See your teacher about anything you still do not understand.)
6 Make a list of any words in **bold** and look these up later in your class notes and textbook.
7 Have a short five-minute break.
8 Start the next double page of work.

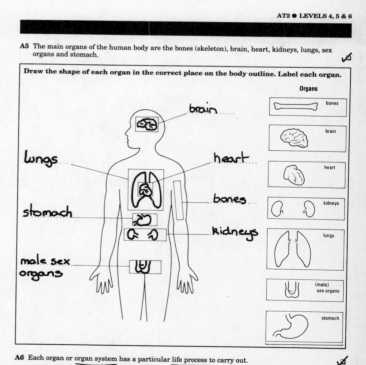

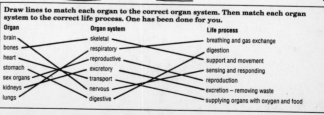

An example of a completed page

Finally, record your revision

Complete this record sheet after each revision session. It will help you to plan your work.

Attainment Target		Session 1 Date completed	Session 2 Date completed	Session 3 Date completed
1 Experimental and investigative science	Foundation A, B			
	Foundation C, D			
	Higher A, B			
	Higher C, D			
2 Life processes and living things	Foundation A, B			
	Foundation C, D, E			
	Higher A, B			
	Higher C, D, E			
3 Materials and their properties	Foundation A, B			
	Foundation C			
	Higher A, B			
	Higher C			
4 Physical processes	Foundation A, B			
	Foundation C, D			
	Foundation E, F			
	Higher A, B			
	Higher C, D			
	Higher E, F			

ATTAINMENT TARGET 1 (Sc1)

Experimental and investigative science

You should be able to plan and carry out investigations in which you:
A ask questions, predict and plan experiments
B observe, alter variables, measure changes and record evidence
C present and interpret results and draw conclusions
D evaluate evidence.

Investigations are practical exercises. You can revise your investigations by reading over your reports about practical work and by remembering what you did, and why you did it.

During this reading, think about the meaning of the words and phrases shown in **bold** on the following pages.

Sc1 FOUNDATION

A1 **Predict** means *work out what will happen.* ❑

Predict which container will be hottest after 5 minutes (tick your answer).

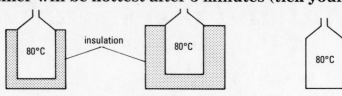

A2 Use **prior knowledge** means *use what you already know.* ❑

For example, you wear clothes made from warm materials in winter.

Use this prior knowledge to name two materials that could be used to insulate this container of hot liquid.

1 ....

2 ....

A3 Formulate a **hypothesis** means *make a prediction that can be tested in an experiment.* ❑

For example, a baker notices that dough rises by different amounts on different days. His hypothesis is that dough rises best at 35 °C.

Describe how you could test this hypothesis fairly.

A4 Optimum conditions mean *the conditions that are best or most favourable.* ❑

Write in the optimum conditions for human life.

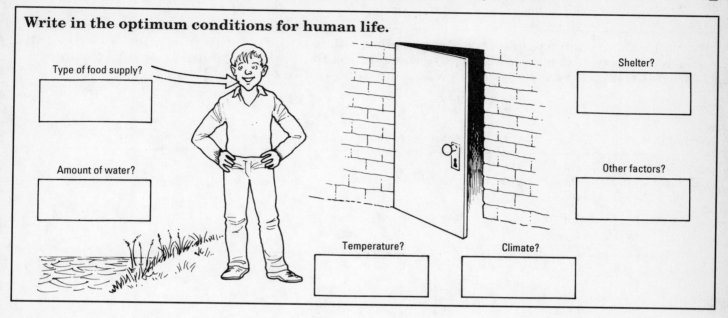

Type of food supply?

Amount of water?

Shelter?

Other factors?

Temperature?

Climate?

A5 Observe means *look carefully at what happens.* ❑

What would you observe in the reaction between acid and chalk?

A6 Variable means *something that affects the result of an experiment when it changes.* ❑

Underline the variables that affect the rate of reaction of chalk and acid.

volume of acid   temperature   time of day   size of chalk pieces   sex of experimenter   colour of beaker

A7 Range of a variable means *using values between sensible lowest (minimum) and highest (maximum) values.* ❑

If you wish to measure the effect of temperature on a living thing whose normal body temperature is 37 °C, then the temperature

variable should range between .... and ....

A8 An independent variable means that *the value is chosen by the experimenter.*

A **dependent variable** means that *its value depends on the value of the independent variable.*

The rate of many reactions increases with temperature. In an experiment, you can change the temperature and measure the time that the reaction takes. This graph shows the kind of result you might expect. ❑

Label one axis as the independent variable and the other as the dependent variable.

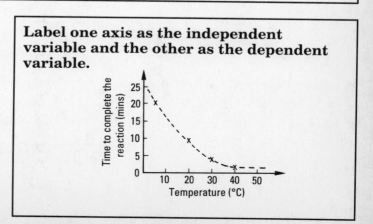

Time to complete the reaction (mins)

Temperature (°C)

A9 The **relative effect** of variables means that *the variables are being compared; some will have a bigger effect on the result than others.*

> **Animals of the same species in different places have bodies of different sizes. To show the relative effects of the key variables below on human body size, write (1) next to the most important, (2) next to the second most important and so on.**
>
> population density ....   light intensity ....   air pollution ....
>
> amount of food ....   type of government ....   education ....

A10 **Key variable** means *a variable that must be taken into account in the design of an experiment, or else the results will not be useful.*

A control means that *one experiment is used to compare the others with; each of the other experiments will have a different key variable changed.*

> **Examine this control.**
>
>
>
> **Write down the key variables that are being tested when each experiment below is compared with the control.**
>
> 2M acid   1M acid   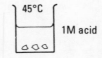 1M acid   1M acid
>
> ....

A11 **Fair test** means *changing one variable in an experiment and keeping all others the same so that the comparison is fair.*

> **Circle the two beakers that can be used as a fair test of the effect of temperature on the rate of reaction.**
>
>
>
> beakers contain 1 mol dm^{-3} acid
> lump chalk
> powdered chalk

B1 **Fine discrimination** in measurement means that *you read the smallest part of the scale of the measuring instrument.*

Using fine discrimination, the length of this object is 52 mm, not 5 cm.

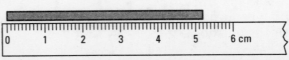

C1 Cause and effect (causal link) means that *you use scientific knowledge or theory to explain why things have happened.*

For example, the dinosaurs disappeared from the Earth millions of years ago. Three possible causes for this effect are that

- a big meteorite hit the Earth
- epidemic diseases killed them
- the climate changed suddenly. ❏

C2 Theory means *a system of ideas that can explain observations and measurements.*

For example, the rate of reaction of chalk with acid increases when the concentration of acid is increased. ❏

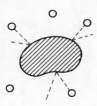 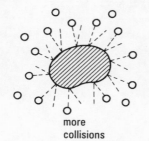

more
collisions

> **With the aid of another drawing, use the particle theory to explain how the rate of reaction would change if the chalk was broken into small pieces and added to acid.**

C3 Qualitative means that *you describe distinct changes.*

Using your senses you can make qualitative descriptions of colour, cloudiness and taste. ❏

> **Name three more factors that can be described qualitatively.**
>
> 1 .... 2 .... 3 ....

C4 Quantitative means that *you measure changes accurately and use numbers to indicate any differences.*

Using instruments you can make quantitative measurements of changes in temperature, volume and length. ❏

> **Name three more factors that can be described quantitatively.**
>
> 1 .... 2 .... 3 ....

C5 Conclusion means *working out what the results mean.* ❏

Write two conclusions from this table of results.

Time (min)	Temperature with nylon cover (°C)	Temperature with woollen cover (°C)
0	80	81
30	63	74
60	48	67
90	33	61
120	25	55
150	25	50

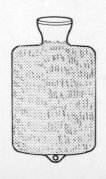

1 ....
....
....
....

2 ....
....
....
....

C6 Using a **model** means *representing an idea or a theory with something that you can see and think about easily.* ❏

> **Draw the model of the particle theory that you used in class.**

C7 A **relationship** between variables means that *the variables change together.*

For example, this graph shows that variable *y* goes up when *x* goes up. ❏

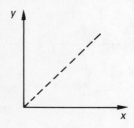

> **Draw a graph to show variable *y* going down as *x* goes up.**
>
> (graph with axes labelled *y* and *x*)

C8 Results can be **recorded** in different ways, such as:

a table, which has
- *a title*
- *rows*
- *columns with titles*

a bar graph, which has
- *a title*
- *two labelled axes with units*
- *bars of same thickness*
- *straight lines for axes*

a line graph, which has
- *a title*
- *two labelled axes with units*
- *numbers on axes*
- *straight lines for axes* ❏

Thickness of insulator (mm)	Temperature after 10 min (°C)
2	60
4	63
6	67
8	70
10	74

effect of thickness

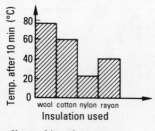

effect of insulator

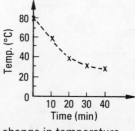

change in temperature

> **Write a conclusion from each set of results given above.**
>
> ....
> ....
> ....

D1 Evaluate means *thinking about how likely it is that a conclusion is correct.* ❏

Evaluating each explanation given below, giving each one a star rating from ★ (poor) to ★★★ (very good).

Dough might rise faster at higher temperatures because:

a) the yeast makes more carbon dioxide gas ………

c) the carbon dioxide gas bubbles expand when hot ………

b) the yeast breathes in and out more quickly ………

d) the water in the dough boils ………

Sc1 HIGHER

A1 **Scientific law** means that *a theory has given many predictions that have always been proved correct.*

Mendel's ideas about heredity were worked out from his studies of pea plants.   ❏

Look at these results. Which law of heredity do they support?

Parents	Round seeds	Wrinkled seeds
F_1 generation	all round	(none)
F_2 generation	5474	1850

(ratio 2.96 : 1)

A2 **Secondary sources** means that *the knowledge is learned from a description of someone else's original work.*

For example, the significance of Gregor Mendel's work was only recognised after his death, when several biologists read his original paper and included his ideas and results in their own writings. ❏

A3 A **mechanism** means *the way in which something happens.*

For example, the mechanism of inheritance is thought to involve chromosomes. The chromosomes carry two alleles for each characteristic. During meiosis, these two alleles are separated and a gamete is formed with only one set of alleles.   ❏

Complete the diagram to show how this mechanism explains why there is an equal chance of humans having a baby girl or boy.

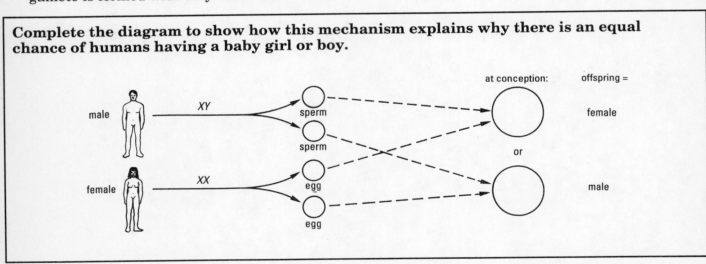

A4 **Abstract concepts** means *ideas that are theoretical and do not deal with real objects or substances.*   ❏

Underline the abstract concepts:

corrosion   atom   oxygen   acid   hydrogen   ion   pH

A5 Systematically means *to do something in an orderly and methodical way.* ❏

Describe how you would systematically investigate this prediction about the inheritance of normal wings in *Drosophila* (fruit fly):

Hypothesis:
Normal wing (W) dominant over miniature wing (w).

Prediction:
Given parent populations of WW and ww, all F_1 offspring will be Ww. F_2 offspring will be WW, Ww and ww in the genotypic ratio 1 : 2 : 1.

Investigation:

normal wing

miniature wing

A6 A **strategy** for investigations means that *you should work out a plan.*

For example, you are investigating the best conditions for growing plants in a greenhouse. Your strategy should include:

- setting up a control plant
- identifying key variables that might affect the growth of the plants (these could be worked out from prior knowledge of photosynthesis, for example, light, temperature, CO_2 level)
- setting up batches of experimental plants to measure the effect of changing each key variable. ❏

Draw up an outline plan for such an investigation.

A7 Manipulate means *to change in a pre-planned way*.

For example, in the greenhouse investigation (A6, on page 9), you can manipulate the amount of light by covering all the windows with black paper and installing an electric lamp that you can switch on and off. Otherwise your results will be affected by the weather; there is more light on sunny days than on cloudy days. ❏

Describe how you could manipulate temperature in the greenhouse investigation.

A8 Showing **creativity** and **invention** means *inventing your own ways of doing things*. ❏

How would you investigate the link between smoking and ill-health?

B1 Valid data means that *the data measures what it is supposed to measure*.

For example, in an investigation of the corrosion of aluminium cooking pots, it would be valid to study the reaction of aluminium with acids and alkalis between pH 4 and pH 11, the range of pH found in foods. It would not be valid to measure the corrosion at pH 1. ❏

Tick the other valid measures of aluminium corrosion in this investigation.

amount of corrosion in steel saucepans ....   amount of corrosion on light aircraft wings ....

amount of corrosion on kitchen foil ....   amount of corrosion at temperatures in the range 25–250 °C ....

B2 Reliable data means that *the data has been collected scientifically and is accurate.*

For example, in the aluminium investigation (B1, on page 10), the data would be reliable if the amount of corrosion was estimated from conductivity measurements. It would not be reliable if you asked your friend to hit the aluminium with a hammer and to describe the noise. ❏

B3 Precision means *to be exact and thorough.* ❏

Describe two ways in which the precision of the smoking investigation (A8, page 10) could have been improved.

1 ....

....

....

2 ....

....

....

B4 A suitable **degree of accuracy** means *the accuracy of the measuring instrument should be matched to the kind of measurement it has to make.* ❏

Draw lines to match the kind of measurement with the instrument needed to achieve a suitable degree of accuracy.

height of a pot plant	micrometer
height of a fir tree	30 cm ruler
length of a leaf	metre stick
thickness of a leaf	10 m tape

C1 Analyse means *to examine your results closely to find out what they mean.* ❏

Analyse these results which show the amount of corrosion of aluminium at different pH values. (No written answer required.)

pH	2	3	4	5	6	7	8	9	10
corrosion of Al	✓✓✓	✓	✓✓✓	✓✓	✓	✓	✓	✗	✗

C2 Justify means *to give a good reason for something.*

If you have to justify aspects of your investigation then be prepared to explain why you did something in a particular way. ❏

C3 A generalisation is *a statement that applies to many similar instances.* ❏

> **Tick the statements that are true generalisations.**
>
> living cells contain water ....
>
> people have hairy heads ....
>
> sickle-cell anaemia is inherited ....
>
> metals corrode in air ....

C4 Interpret means *to explain the meaning of your results.* ❏

> **What is your interpretation of the results given in C1 on the previous page?**

D1 Limitations of evidence means that *any experiment has shortcomings and weaknesses, and experimental results must not be relied on completely.*

For example, in the greenhouse investigation (A6, page 9), the experimental evidence is limited by uncontrollable factors like the effect of insects on individual plants, the health of individual plants or the draft of air which is different in different parts of the greenhouse. ❏

D2 Sources of error means *the defects in an experiment that cause inaccuracies in the results.* ❏

> **What is the major source of error in experiments carried out in school laboratories?**

D3 Scientific **controversy** means that *scientists disagree about something*.

For example, the theory of evolution has always been controversial. ❏

Write down two examples of modern scientific controversies (maybe from a newspaper article or a TV programme).

1 .... 2 ....

....

....

....

....

D4 Critically evaluate means *to search carefully for any faults in something, and if necessary work out how it might be improved.* ❏

Critically evaluate this study of smoking conducted by an expensive 'youth' magazine.

All readers were asked to return a questionnaire which asked them about their personal smoking habits. 2000 did so. From this, the magazine concluded that only 15% of British teenagers smoked, and none had health problems.

D5 Anomalous result means *a result that is atypical and does not fit the pattern of the other results.* ❏

> **Circle the anomalous result in C1 on page 11.**

D6 Probability means *the chance or likelihood of something happening*.

For example, the probability of the Sun rising tomorrow is nearly 1 chance in 1. The probability of an apple containing a worm is about 1 in 1000. The probability of a tree saying 'good morning' is maybe 1 in $10^{trillion}$ ❏

Estimate the probability of the following things happening.

a) throwing two heads in a row when tossing a coin ....

b) dying before the age of 50 because you smoke ....

c) having two grandchildren with blue eyes ....

d) passing all your GCSEs ....

ATTAINMENT TARGET 2 (Sc2)
Life processes and living things

Sc2 FOUNDATION

A1 All living things are made of cells. ❑

A2 Most animal cells have the same basic parts: cell membrane, cytoplasm and nucleus.

Most plant cells have the same basic parts: cell wall, cell membrane, cytoplasm, nucleus, vacuole and chloroplasts. ❑

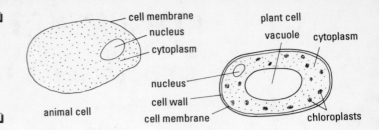

Circle the animal cells using one colour; circle the plant cells using a different colour. Complete the colour key.

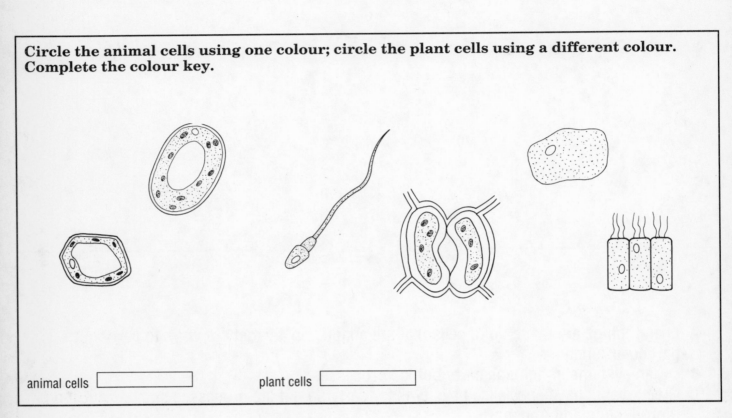

animal cells ☐   plant cells ☐

A3 Each cell part has a particular job (function). ❑

Complete the statements with the name of the correct cell part listed in A2.

In both animal and plant cells:

• the .... controls what enters and leaves the cell

• chemical reactions take place in the ....

• the .... controls cell activity (for example, cell division) and carries the genes that can be passed on to the next generation.

Plant cells also contain:

• ...., the site of photosynthesis

• a .... containing cell sap, which gives the cell shape and provides support for the plant

• a .... that surrounds the membrane and provides support for the cell and therefore the whole plant.

A4 In **multicellular** organisms cells develop in different ways depending on the job they will have. So, the final structure of a cell depends on its function. For example:

- cells that take in, pass out or carry substances tend to have a large surface area

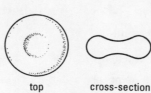

top   cross-section

human red blood cells
carry oxygen

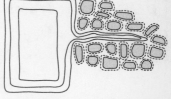

plant root hair cells absorb
water from the soil

- cells that form linings or coverings tend to be flat.

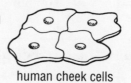

human cheek cells

leaf epidermal cells

Write a description of each cell in the cell structure box. Label three parts of an animal cell on the neurone and on the sperm cell. Label six parts of a plant cell on the leaf palisade cell.

Cell structure

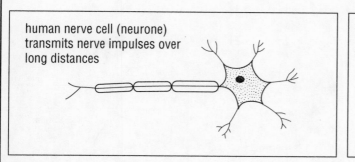

human nerve cell (neurone)
transmits nerve impulses over
long distances

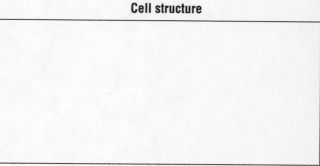

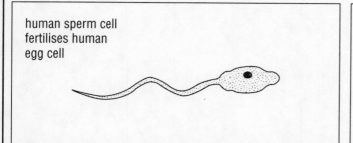

human sperm cell
fertilises human
egg cell

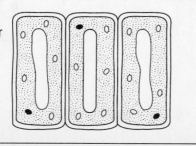

leaf palisade cell
traps sunlight for
photosynthesis

A5 In multicellular organisms the cells are organised into **tissues**, **organs** and **systems** and carry out particular life processes. ❏

Draw lines to match the level of cell organisation with the correct description.

Level of cell organisation	Description
tissue	a group of organs and tissues carrying out one life process
organ	a group of cells with the same structure and function
system	a structure, made up of several different tissues, which carries out one particular function

A6 The main organs of the human body are the bones (skeleton), brain, heart, kidneys, lungs, sex organs and stomach. ❏

Draw the shape of each organ in the correct place on the body outline. Label each organ.

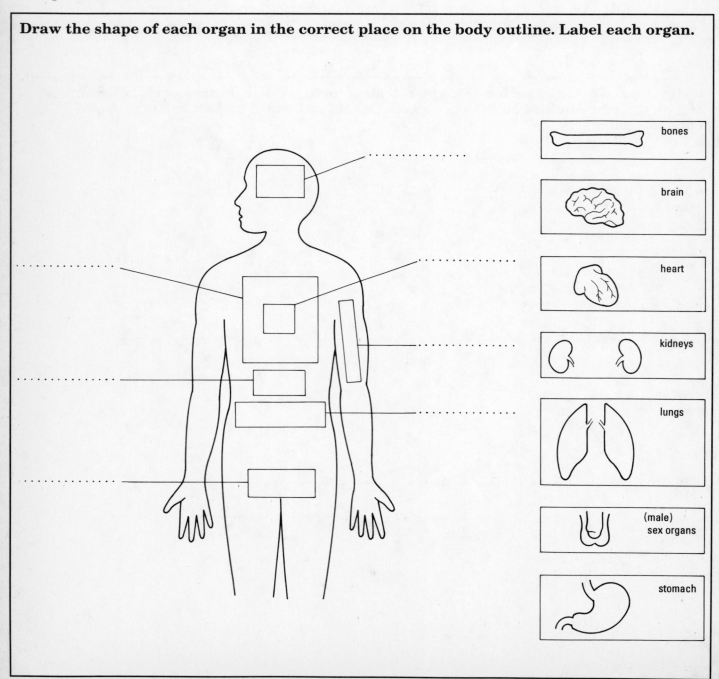

A7 Each organ or organ system has a particular life process to carry out.

Draw lines to match each organ to the correct organ system. Then match each organ system to the correct life process. One has been done for you. Use a different colour each time.

Organ	Organ system	Life process
brain	skeletal	breathing and gas exchange
bones	respiratory	digestion
heart	reproductive	support and movement
stomach	excretory	sensing and responding
sex organs	transport	reproduction
kidneys	nervous	excretion – removing waste
lungs	digestive	supplying organs with oxygen and food

A8 Each organ system has a particular function.

Use the words from the word list to complete each statement.

arteries   brain   digestion   heart   kidneys   lungs   nerves   ovaries   oxygen   protect   sperm   support

1 Blood is pumped by the .... to all body organs through .... and capillaries. This provides the organs with food and oxygen. Blood transports waste from cells and returns to the heart in veins.

2 The bones of the skeleton provide .... and .... the organs. The muscles attached to bones allow movement to take place.

3 Large, insoluble food particles are broken down in the process of .... into smaller, soluble particles by enzymes. This process takes place mainly in the stomach and small intestine, at which point the soluble food passes into the bloodstream. Undigested food passes along the large intestine and is egested at the anus.

4 Waste products in the blood are removed by the .... and stored in the bladder before being excreted.

5 The .... collects information sent to it via certain .... and enables us to respond by sending messages to the muscles.

6 Air is breathed into the .... where .... is exchanged for carbon dioxide. Movement of the rib-cage and diaphragm causes the lungs to inflate and deflate.

7 Egg cells are produced in the .... of females and .... cells are produced in the testes of males. Fertilisation occurs when a sperm cell and egg cell meet and fuse (join up).

A9 The main organs of a flowering plant are the **roots**, **stem**, **leaves** and **flower**. Within the flower the main organs are the **stamens** and the **ovary**. ❑

Label the organs of the flowering plant below. Draw lines to match each organ to its function.

Function

to enable the plant to reproduce; stamens produce the male pollen and eggs are produced in the ovary

to carry out photosynthesis

to support leaves and flowers and allow materials to be transported through plant

to anchor plant in soil and take up water and mineral salts from the soil

A10 Some life processes in plants and animals are the same. ❑

Complete the table by making a tick in the correct column.

Life process	Animals and plants	Plants only	Animals only
• gas exchange			
• reproduction			
• responding to the environment			
• transport			
• excretion			
• movement			
• digestion			
• photosynthesis			

B1 All animals must eat to stay alive. There are three stages in the nutrition of animals:

- feeding or obtaining food
- digestion
- using the food and getting rid of waste.

Vertebrate animals take food into their mouths and break it up mechanically using teeth or beaks. ❑

B2 In digestion, large, insoluble molecules are broken down chemically by the action of a group of proteins called **enzymes** into smaller, soluble molecules. In humans, some digestion takes place in the mouth before the food is passed down the gullet or oesophagus by **peristalsis** to the stomach. Here, more digestion takes place and the food is churned up. It then passes to the small intestine where enzymes produced in the pancreas complete the process of chemical digestion. Soluble food is absorbed into blood capillaries for transport first to the liver, then to all parts of the body. Undigested food moves through the large intestine where excess water is absorbed into the blood supply. The remaining waste is egested at the anus.

Complete the flow chart of digestion by writing the words below in the correct boxes and joining them with arrows. Draw lines from the flow chart to label the parts of the human digestive system. Add a word from the passage above to describe what happens in each part.

anus   gullet (oesophagus)   large intestine   mouth   pancreas   small intestine   stomach

structure   what happens

liver

gall
bladder

structure

what happens

B3 Each food type (the **substrate**) is broken down by specific enzymes that work best in particular conditions. All enzyme-controlled reactions follow the same pattern:

$$\text{substrate} + \text{enzyme} \rightarrow \text{product} + \text{enzyme}$$

Use a different colour to highlight or circle each substrate and its *final* products of digestion.

Substrate	Where broken down	Enzymes involved	Product	Conditions required
starch	mouth	amylase	maltose	slightly alkaline
	small intestine	amylases	glucose	slightly alkaline
protein	stomach	pepsin	polypeptides	acidic
	small intestine	proteases	amino acids	slightly alkaline
fat	small intestine	lipases	fatty acids and glycerol	slightly alkaline

B4 Hydrochloric acid makes the pH of the stomach acidic. This helps to destroy any bacteria ingested. Bile salts produced in the liver and stored in the gall bladder are passed to the small intestine where they create alkaline conditions. ❑

Which digestive enzyme requires a low pH? ....

Which three groups of digestive enzymes require a high pH?

....

B5 Digested food is transported to every cell of the body where it can be used in one of several ways, including:

- as a source of energy
- for growth and repair. ❑

B6 The human circulatory system is made up of the heart and blood vessels. The heart is a double pump made of **muscle**. Each side has a collecting chamber called an **atrium** (or **auricle**) and a pumping chamber called a **ventricle**. **Valves** in the heart control the direction of blood flow. The **right side** collects blood **from the body** and pumps blood **to the lungs** only, to collect oxygen. The **left side** collects oxygen-rich blood **from the lungs** and pumps this **to the body**. ❑

Complete the diagram of the heart by:

- **labelling the four chambers**
- **writing *to lungs, from lungs, to body, from body* in the correct boxes**
- **colouring the side of the heart containing oxygen-rich blood red and the side with de-oxygenated blood blue.**

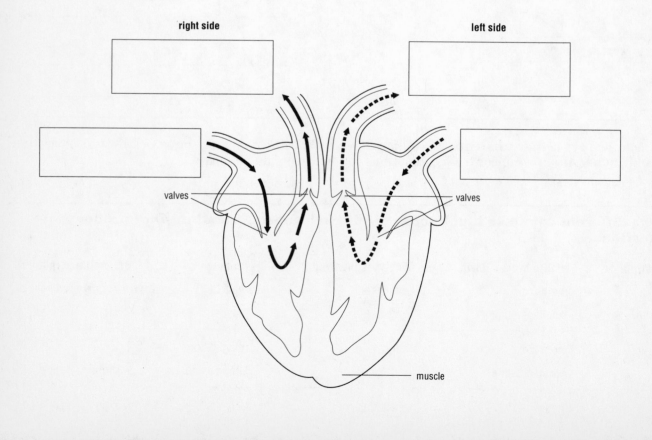

B7 Blood is contained within blood vessels called **arteries**, **capillaries** and **veins**. Arteries carry blood away from the heart. Veins carry blood back to the heart. Arteries and veins are joined by tiny vessels called capillaries. ❑

Label the arteries and veins on the heart diagram in B6.
Label the artery, vein and capillaries on the diagram below.

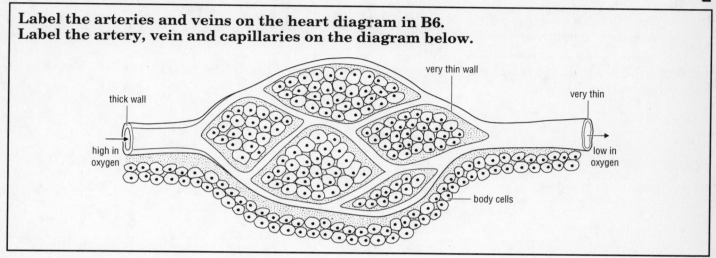

B8 Blood is made up of a liquid called **plasma**, fragments of cells called **platelets** and **red and white blood cells**. Red cells, which do not have a nucleus, contain the red pigment **haemoglobin**, which carries oxygen to all cells. White blood cells have a nucleus and either attack and digest microbes or produce antibodies that destroy infecting microbes. They can leave the blood vessels to seek out germs. Platelets are needed to stop bleeding from cuts by helping a clot, then a scab, to form. Plasma carries digested food, dissolved carbon dioxide gas and antibodies. ❑

Label each drawing and describe what each part does in a few words in the space below each drawing.

B9 Energy is released from food in the process of aerobic cellular respiration. In most organisms this involves oxygen and food interacting to produce carbon dioxide and water. Energy is stored in chemical form. ❑

Complete the word equation for respiration.

glucose + ... $\xrightarrow[\text{released}]{\text{energy}}$ .... + water

$C_6H_{12}O_6$ + $6O_2$ $\xrightarrow[\text{released}]{\text{energy}}$ $6CO_2$ + $6H_2O$

B10 The process of aerobic respiration uses oxygen and produces carbon dioxide. These gases are exchanged in the lungs, which is why inhaled (breathed-in) air is different from exhaled air. Air travels through the nose, down the **trachea** and **bronchi** to the **bronchioles** of the lungs. Each bronchiole ends in an air sac (made of many thin-walled **alveoli**). Here, gas exchange takes place; oxygen diffuses from the air sac into blood capillaries, and carbon dioxide and water vapour **diffuse** in the opposite direction. ❏

Write *inhaled* and *exhaled* in the correct places in the table. Then label the main parts of the respiratory system.

Gas	....	....
nitrogen	79.00%	79.00%
oxygen	20.00%	16.00%
carbon dioxide	0.04%	4.00%
water vapour	low	high

lung

heart

B11 Humans respond to a range of environmental **stimuli** using a range of **sense organs** or **receptors**. ❏

Complete the table using the word bank. The same word can be used twice.

Sense	Receptor	Stimulus	Word bank
sight			chemicals
hearing			ears
touch			eyes
taste			gravity
smell			inner ear
balance			light
			nose
			pressure
			skin
			sound
			tongue

B12 In humans, responses to environmental stimuli are controlled by the nervous system. The main parts are the brain and spinal cord – called the **central nervous system** (or **CNS**) – and the nerves joining these structures to the rest of the body. There are three types of nerve cells or **neurones**. **Sensory neurones** are attached to the sense organs (receptors) and return information from them to the brain. **Motor neurones** allow the body to respond by taking messages from the brain back to the effector muscles. These two types of neurones are linked by **connector neurones** in the brain or spinal cord.

Most behaviours follow a similar pattern. For example, when you walk into a brightly lit place:

pattern:	stimulus →	receptor →	co-ordinator →	effector → response
example:	light in eye	retina	brain	iris muscles pupil contracts

❏

Copying this pattern, explain another behaviour, for example, moving your leg away from the warmth of a fire.

B13 When we look at an object, light reflected from it enters the eye. The light is focused by the **cornea** and **lens** onto the **retina**. Here light energy is transformed into electrical energy, which passes through the **optic nerve** to the brain. ❏

Label the eye using the words in bold in the paragraph above.

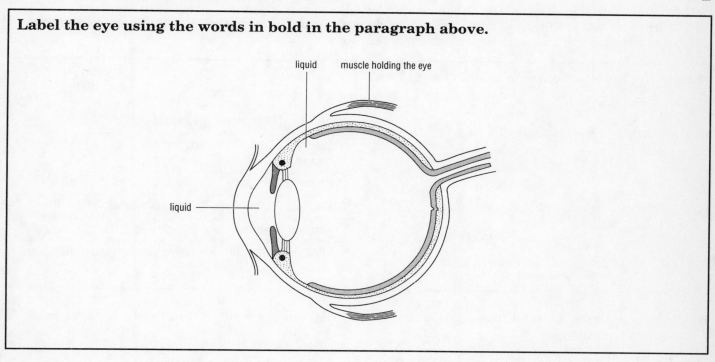

liquid   muscle holding the eye

liquid

B14 The lens changes shape to focus light onto the retina. When looking at a near object the lens is fat. When looking at a distant object the lens is thin. ❏

Draw the expected shape of the lens in the two diagrams below.

Object far away   **Object in middle distance**   **Object close by**

B15 The iris is the coloured part of the eye. It is a circle of muscle with a hole in the middle. This is the pupil. In dark conditions the iris contracts, making the pupil larger. The opposite happens in bright light. ❏

Complete the diagrams to show the size of the pupil in dim and bright light. Label the iris and pupil on the diagram in B13.

| Dim light | Normal light | Bright light |

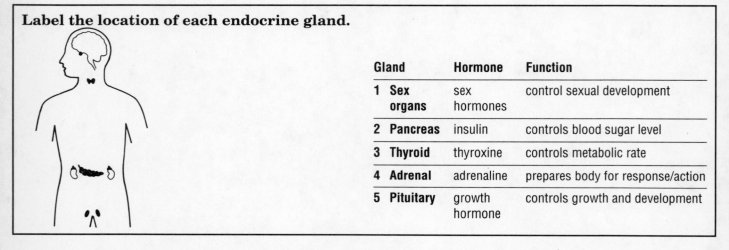

B16 Each human endocrine gland produces different hormones, each with their own function. Hormones are produced in tiny amounts and travel in the bloodstream to specific target organs where they bring about a particular response. ❏

Label the location of each endocrine gland.

	Gland	Hormone	Function
1	**Sex organs**	sex hormones	control sexual development
2	**Pancreas**	insulin	controls blood sugar level
3	**Thyroid**	thyroxine	controls metabolic rate
4	**Adrenal**	adrenaline	prepares body for response/action
5	**Pituitary**	growth hormone	controls growth and development

B17 Few organisms can tolerate variation in their internal environment. For example, humans must maintain a constant:

- water balance
- body temperature
- blood pH (the amount of carbon dioxide in the blood)
- blood sugar level.

Keeping conditions constant is called **homeostasis**. ❏

Complete the table to show how a constant water balance is maintained in your body.

Water balance	
Gain water by	**Lose water by**

B18 In vertebrate animals the kidneys control water balance. When blood water concentration rises, for example after drinking a lot, less water is reabsorbed by the kidneys and so a larger volume of dilute urine is excreted. The opposite takes place when blood water concentration decreases, for example after eating very salty food. ❏

Describe what happens in the kidneys when blood water concentration decreases. What type of urine is produced?

B19 Humans have several defences against infection:

- skin, which is a barrier to bacteria and viruses
- blood clotting, which seals a wound
- white blood cells, which destroy bacteria
- antibodies made by white cells that help to destroy bacteria and viruses
- mucus in the trachea and bronchi that traps dirt and microbes. ❏

B20 Having a healthy lifestyle means avoiding damaging activities such as smoking and taking drugs. Precautions can be taken to reduce the risk of contracting sexually transmitted diseases, such as AIDS. ❏

C1 In green plants **photosynthesis** is the process in which carbon dioxide and water are combined to produce glucose and oxygen. Light energy from the Sun is needed for this process. Light is trapped by the green pigment **chlorophyll** in the **chloroplasts** of leaf cells. Glucose can be stored as **starch** for later use, used directly as a source of energy for the plant or used to produce other materials for growth (for example, **cellulose** for cell walls). ❏

Complete the word equation for photosynthesis. Then write in the boxes what can happen to the glucose.

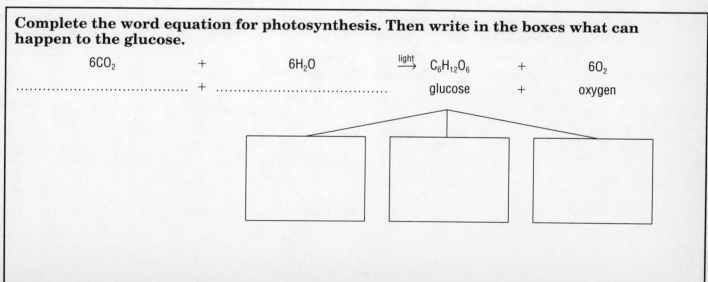

$$6CO_2 \quad + \quad 6H_2O \quad \xrightarrow{light} \quad C_6H_{12}O_6 \quad + \quad 6O_2$$

.... + ... glucose + oxygen

C2 The rate of photosynthesis is limited by the availability of the raw materials and by light intensity. Low light intensity, low carbon dioxide concentration and lack of water all reduce the rate of the process. ❏

Complete the graph to show the effect of an increase in temperature on the rate of photosynthesis.

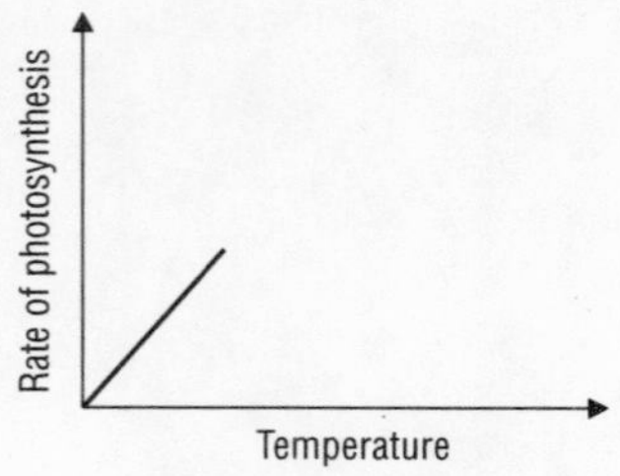

C3 In plants, energy is released when glucose combines with oxygen in the process of aerobic **respiration**. The word equation for respiration is the reverse of the equation for photosynthesis (but light and chlorophyll are *not* required). ❏

Write the word equation for respiration here.

C4 Plants do not get food from the soil but they do absorb **mineral salts** through their root hair cells. Minerals contain elements essential for growth and development. ❏

Match each essential element to its function. Use a different colour each time.

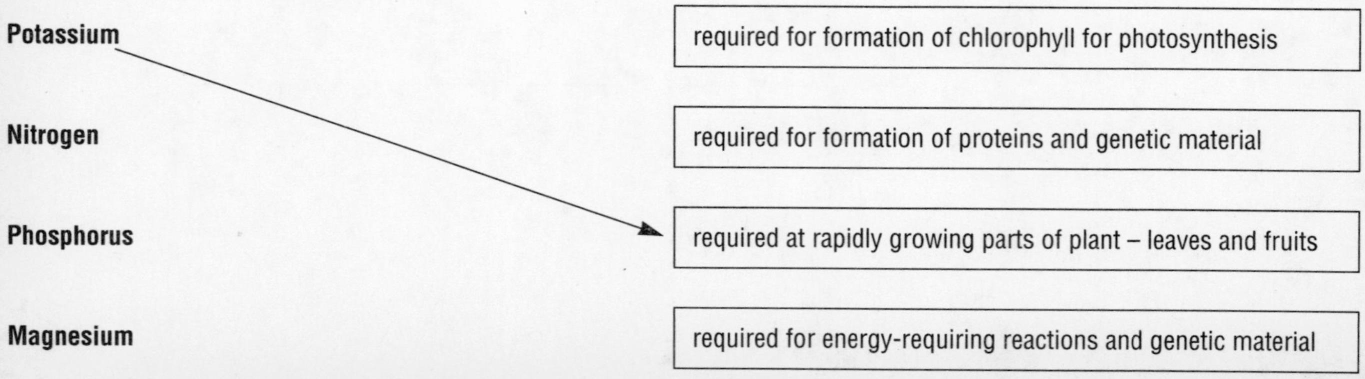

Potassium

Nitrogen

Phosphorus

Magnesium

required for formation of chlorophyll for photosynthesis

required for formation of proteins and genetic material

required at rapidly growing parts of plant – leaves and fruits

required for energy-requiring reactions and genetic material

C5 A range of plant **hormones** is involved in the control of growth and development. A hormone called **IAA** produced at the growing tip of a plant promotes growth here and reduces growth of side stems. It is also involved in the plant's growth response to the direction of light. ❑

Complete each diagram to show how the plants grow.

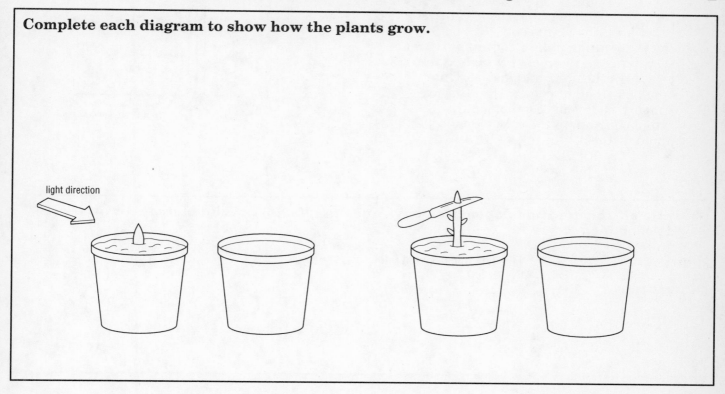

C6 There are many commercial applications of plant hormones:

- rooting powder to promote root formation on cuttings
- spraying with hormones to promote even ripening of fruit. ❑

C7 In green plants, the rate of photosynthesis is greater than the rate of respiration during the day. At night, only respiration takes place. Both processes require an exchange of gases between the cells and the atmosphere. This takes place through tiny holes called **stomata** in the stem and on the lower epidermis of leaves. (Some plants have stomata on upper and lower leaf surfaces.) ❑

Label the diagrams below using the terms *daytime gas exchange* and *night-time gas exchange*.

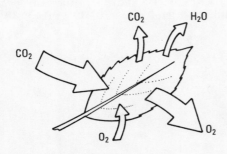

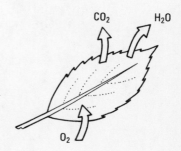

....

C8 Water vapour also escapes through the stomata. This is called **transpiration** and helps the plant in two ways:

- water evaporating from the leaf surface helps keep the plant cool
- the evaporation pulls a continuous stream of water from the roots through **xylem** vessels in the stem and leaves. This supplies all plant cells with water for support, chemical reactions in the cytoplasm and, in the case of leaf cells, photosynthesis. ❏

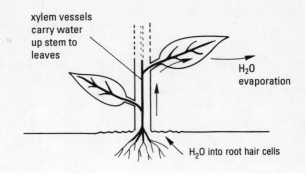

xylem vessels carry water up stem to leaves

H_2O evaporation

H_2O into root hair cells

The rate of transpiration depends on environmental factors. Write *increase* or *decrease* beside each factor.

Factor	Effect on transpiration rate
High temperature	
Low humidity	
Still air	

D1 There are millions of different types or **species** of animals on Earth. Animals of the same species can breed successfully; animals from two different species usually cannot.

When different species have common features they can be grouped into sets. Grouping or classifying allows us to name them in a logical way. ❏

D2 Until recently botanists (plant scientists) classified fungi, such as yeast and mushrooms, and algae, such as seaweed, as plants. These are now considered as two separate kingdoms. ❏

D3 **Genetics** is the study of inherited features or characteristics. Genetic material is held in the form of genes on chromosomes in the nucleus of every cell. In school science we make genetics easier by looking at features that are controlled by only one gene, for example, tongue rolling in humans, coat colour in rabbits and flower colour. ❏

D4 Sex cells (sperm and egg in animals, pollen and egg in plants) are produced in the sex organs. When they join at **fertilisation**, genes on chromosomes from the male and female parents are brought together. In this way genetic information is **inherited** and passed from one generation to the next. ❏

D5 Within a species, for example humans, there is **variation** (differences) between individuals. The variation may be caused by:

- genetics
- environmental factors
- a combination of genetics and environmental factors.

For each feature below, write *genetic* or *environmental* next to each cause of variation.

1 Weight of a newborn baby

Cause of variation

both parents short ....

mother smoked during pregnancy ....

mother ate healthy diet while pregnant ....

2 Growth of pea seedlings

low light intensity ....

acid soil ....

parent plants tall ....

D6 Human cells carry 23 pairs of chromosomes. Sex or **gender** is controlled by one pair of chromosomes called the sex chromosomes. Females have two X sex chromosomes. Males have one X sex chromosome and one Y sex chromosome.

Sperm and egg cells carry one sex chromosome only. This explains how gender is inherited and why, on average, there are an equal number of boys and girls born.

Complete the diagram to show how gender is inherited.

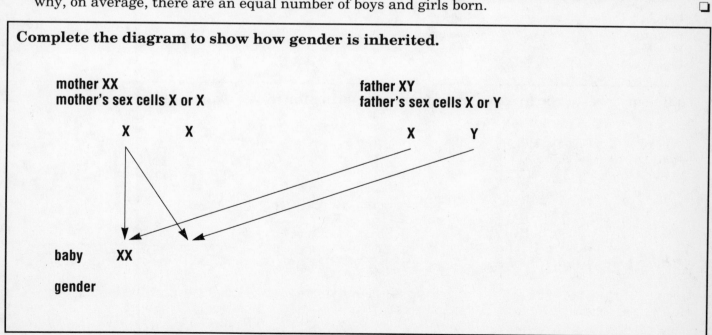

mother XX
mother's sex cells X or X

father XY
father's sex cells X or Y

X   X   X   Y

baby   XX

gender

D7 Over a long period of time one type of organism can develop into a new type of organism. This is called **evolution**. For example it is believed that the ancestors of the modern giraffe had much shorter necks and that the ancestors of modern humans were apes.

D8 Evidence for evolution comes from the **fossil record**. Fossils are preserved forms of organisms found in some sedimentary rocks. These rocks are laid down in layers, so the deeper a fossil is in the rock the older it is. Comparing the structures of similar fossils in different layers gives clues to the evolution of that plant or animal. ❏

Draw an arrow on this cliff face of sedimentary rock. Label one end 'youngest rock' and the other 'oldest rock'.

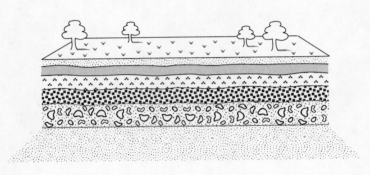

E1 All living things **compete** for resources to stay alive. Competition takes place between organisms of the same species and with other species. When resources are scarce not all the individuals in a population will survive.

Animals compete for:

- food
- water
- space
- mates.

Plants compete for:

- light
- water
- space.

❏

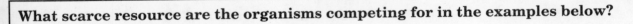

What scarce resource are the organisms competing for in the examples below?

plants on a woodland floor grow and flower in spring before the trees above them burst into leaf

....

for photosynthesis

gannets are seabirds that nest on very narrow ledges on cliffs

....

for reproduction

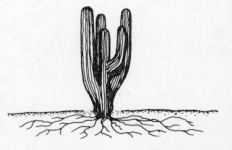

some desert cacti have very large root systems just under the surface of the sand

....

for support and photosynthesis

E2 Animals have **adaptations** that allow them to survive in their natural environment.

Terrestrial (land) animals

- waterproof surface prevents water loss
- able to breathe air
- supporting tissues to give shape and strength
- internal fertilisation for sperm to swim to egg. ❏

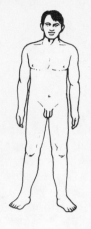
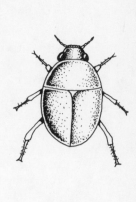

Freshwater animals – fish

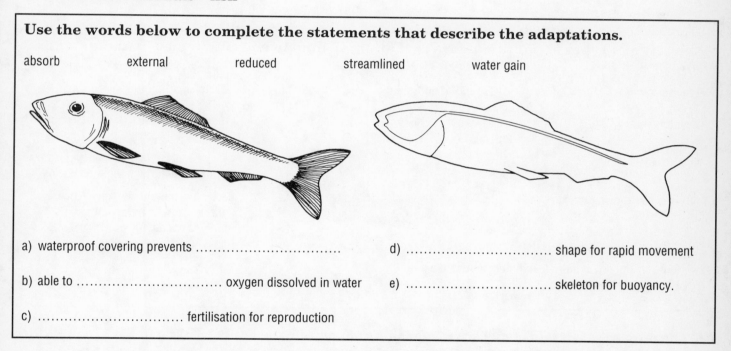

Use the words below to complete the statements that describe the adaptations.

absorb   external   reduced   streamlined   water gain

a) waterproof covering prevents ....

b) able to .... oxygen dissolved in water

c) .... fertilisation for reproduction

d) .... shape for rapid movement

e) .... skeleton for buoyancy.

E3 Plants are also adapted to survive in their natural habitats. For example, desert plants have adaptations to obtain and store as much water as possible and lose as little as possible. ❏

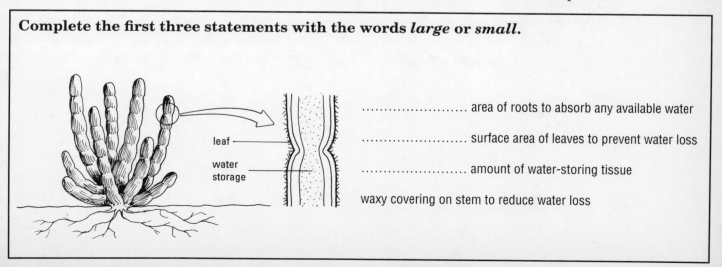

Complete the first three statements with the words *large* or *small*.

leaf

water storage

.... area of roots to absorb any available water

.... surface area of leaves to prevent water loss

.... amount of water-storing tissue

waxy covering on stem to reduce water loss

E4 A population grows when the birth rate is greater than the death rate. Population decline can be caused by:

- environmental resources such as oxygen and food becoming limited
- disease
- the activity of predators.

For example, the number of bacteria in a sealed culture vessel will increase rapidly at first when lots of food and oxygen are available. When these resources become more limited the numbers increase more slowly. Finally, the numbers fall as the resources are used up and as waste within the culture builds up. ❏

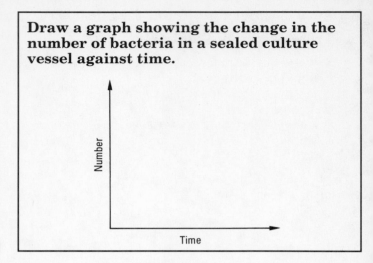

Draw a graph showing the change in the number of bacteria in a sealed culture vessel against time.

E5 Some human activity produces substances that pollute the air, water and soil. ❏

What type or types of pollution does each of these human activities cause? (Air, water or soil.)

Human activity	Type(s) of pollution	Effects of pollution
burning fuels	....	produces acid rain that damages plants and acidifies water
mining creates spoil tips	....	heavy metals in the tips poison plants and animals through the food chain
untreated sewage passes into sea	....	bacteria in sewage reduce oxygen concentration of water, and nutrients encourage growth of poison-producing algae

Two more examples of human activities that cause pollution:

1 .... 2 ....

E6 The presence of certain organisms in a habitat can indicate the level of pollution. For example, the level of air pollution can be indicated by which lichens are growing in a habitat. The types of invertebrates living in a freshwater habitat give an indication of the level of pollution there. ❏

E7 Environmental damage can be caused by the build-up of human waste, by industrial processes and by over-exploitation as a result of economic factors such as the demand for food and fossil fuels. ❏

Draw lines to match each human activity with two consequences. Use a different colour each time.

Human activity	Consequences
obtaining and burning fossil fuels	over-use of fertilisers causing water pollution
producing food	formation of spoil tips causing land pollution
	release of greenhouse gases and creation of acid rain
	destruction of habitats for farmland

E8 An **ecosystem** consists of a community of living organisms and its interactions with the physical features of its environment, such as weather, soil or water type. An ecosystem is kept in balance by the flow of energy through **food chains** and by cycling important biological raw materials such as carbon and nitrogen to keep them at a steady level. Anything that upsets the balance damages the ecosystem. ❏

E9 In any ecosystem there are many food chains. A food chain shows the food source of each animal in the chain. Every food chain starts with a green plant. Different words are used to describe the plants and animals in a food chain, and all food chains follow the same basic pattern shown below.

Note: animals that eat both plant material and animal material are called **omnivores**. ❏

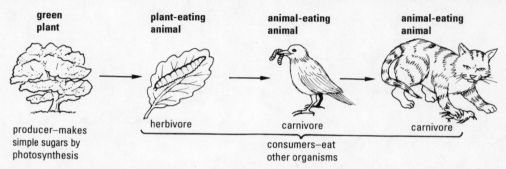

In each of the food chains below:

1 label the *producers* and *consumers*
2 circle the herbivores using one colour and the carnivores using another. Make a colour key.

colour key

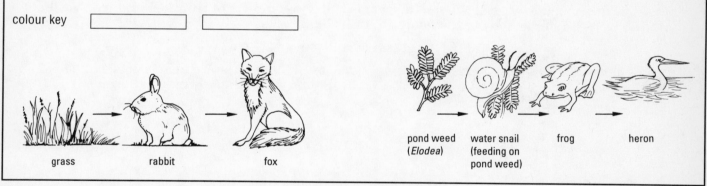

E10 Two more words are used to describe animals in a food chain: **predator** and **prey**. Predators are carnivores that eat other (live) animals – their prey. Sometimes a predator can be the prey of another, bigger predator. ❏

E11 A large change in the numbers of any organism in a food chain has 'knock-on' effects on the other organisms in the chain.

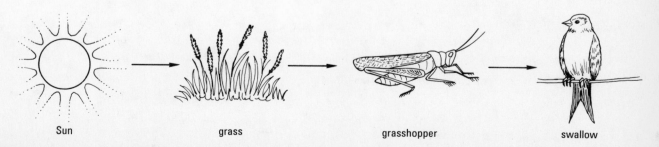

For example, in the food chain above, if many insects are killed by **insecticides** there is less food for the swallows and less damage to the green plants. ❏

Complete the sentence below the food chain with the words *increase, decrease, less* **and** *herbivores*. **(You may use a word more than once.)**

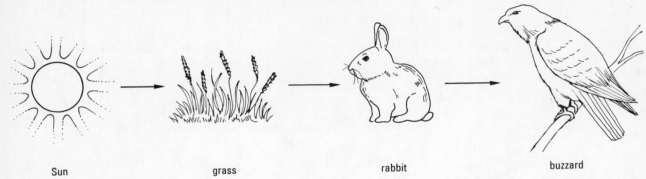

Sun   grass   rabbit   buzzard

If disease killed many of the rabbits there would be .... food for the buzzards and their population

would .... There would be .... damage to the plants so plant growth

would .... providing more food for other ....

E12 Energy transfer in a food chain can be estimated in two ways:

- by counting the number of organisms at each point in the chain
- by measuring the mass of organisms (the **biomass**) at each point in the chain.

These measurements can be shown in diagrams called **pyramids of number** and **pyramids of biomass**. For example, look at the following food chain:

$$Sun \rightarrow grass\ seeds \rightarrow mouse \rightarrow owl$$

The number of organisms at each point gets smaller.

The total biomass of organisms gets smaller even though individuals may get bigger. ❏

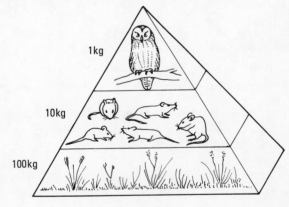

1kg

10kg

100kg

E13 Decomposers are an important group of consumers in an ecosystem. Their job is to bring about the decay of dead organisms and so to return important biological materials to the soil. They allow materials such as carbon and nitrogen to be cycled through the ecosystem.

There are three main groups of decomposers:

- bacteria   • fungi   • soil invertebrates.   ❏

E14 Decay is fastest when the decomposing material is broken up or shredded and lying in a fairly tightly packed pile. The pile needs to be warm and moist. These conditions favour the growth of fungi and an increase in numbers of bacteria. Gardeners make compost heaps to decay garden waste into useful compost.   ❏

E15 Certain microbes can decompose biological material. Microbes are used to help purify water in sewage works. One group of microbes digests solid material in the settle tanks and a second group digests any remaining biological (organic) material as water passes through the filter beds. ❏

Label the *settle tank* and *filter bed* in the diagram.

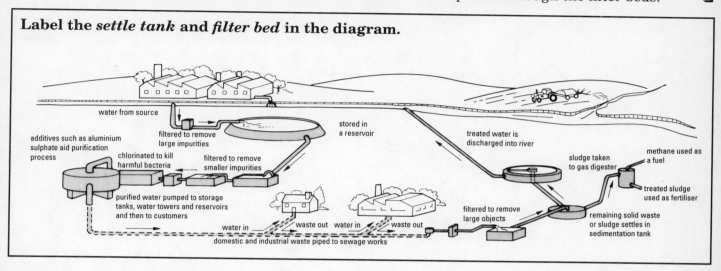

E16 Carbon is the building block of all biological chemicals. It is cycled through the ecosystem as carbon dioxide. Two biological processes keep the level of carbon dioxide steady – **photosynthesis** in green plants and **respiration** in all living organisms.

Human activities, such as burning fossil fuels, are upsetting the balance by adding carbon dioxide to the atmosphere. ❏

Label *photosynthesis* and *respiration* in the diagrams below.

1 .... 2 ....

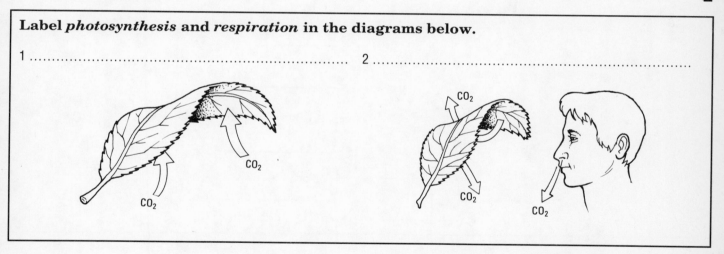

E17 The element nitrogen is present in many biological chemicals such as proteins and genetic material (DNA). Nitrogen from the atmosphere is passed to the soil where bacteria make it available to plants. From here it passes to animals through the food chain. The decomposition of dead plants and animals cycles nitrogen back through the soil. Some is returned to the air by the action of certain bacteria. ❏

Complete the flow chart with the words *bacteria*, *death and decay*, *food chain* and *lightning*. (You may use a word more than once.)

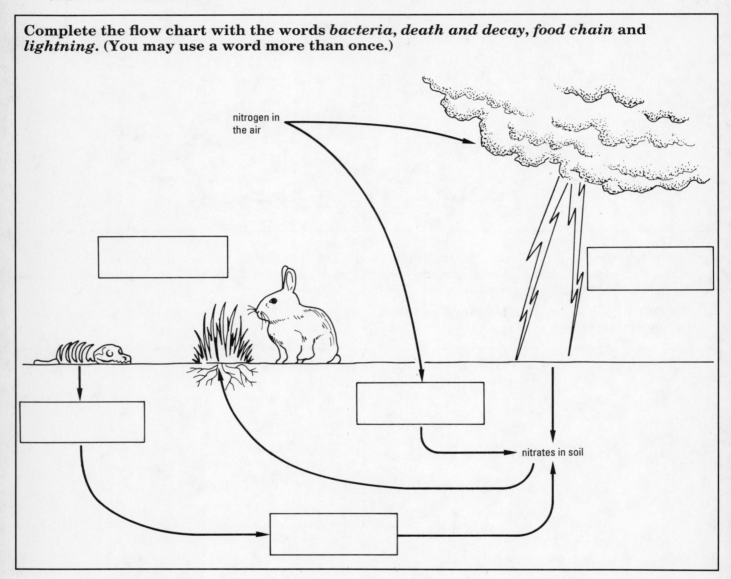

A1 Solutes move into cells along a **concentration gradient** by **diffusion**. In diffusion solutes always move from higher to lower concentration. This is how food and oxygen enter cells from blood capillaries and how wastes and carbon dioxide (CO_2) enter the blood from cells.

Label the diagram using the words in the word bank.

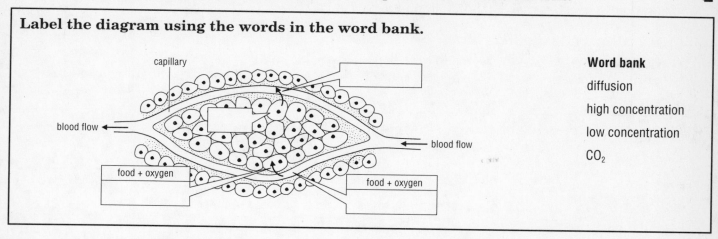

Word bank

diffusion

high concentration

low concentration

CO_2

A2 The movement of water into and out of a cell across the cell membrane is called **osmosis**. Cell membranes are semi-permeable – only some substances can pass through them. Water moves by osmosis from an area where it is in relatively high concentration across a cell membrane to an area where the water concentration is lower. Water concentration depends on the amount of **solute** present. Pure water has the highest water concentration, seawater has a much lower water concentration because it contains dissolved salts.

For example, the shape of red blood cells depends on osmosis.

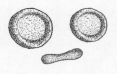 

in normal conditions water
in and out is in balance

in higher water concentration
water moves in by osmosis

If the water concentration of the blood plasma becomes higher than the water concentration of the red blood cells, water enters the cells and they swell up. If this continues the cells eventually burst.

Complete each of the diagrams above with an arrow to show the direction of movement of water.

A3 Cells require some substances to be at a higher concentration inside the cell than outside. They must obtain these against the concentration gradient. This process requires energy and is called **active transport**.

**Draw an arrow to show the direction of movement of sodium ions into the animal cell.
Label this *active transport*.**

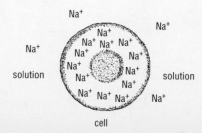

A4 Genetic information is held on structures called **chromosomes** in the nucleus of the cell. Human body cells have 46 chromosomes, cabbage cells have 18. Chromosomes are involved in the process of cell division. During division, they are visible through a microscope. When cells are not dividing the chromosomes become very long and thin and cannot be seen easily. ❏

A5 There are two types of cell division:

- **mitosis**, which increases the number of cells for growth and tissue repair
- **meiosis**, which produces sex cells for reproduction (each sex cell has half the full chromosome number). ❏

Complete the blanks in the table below comparing mitosis and meiosis.

	Mitosis	Meiosis
Function		
Location	growing points of plants and animals	sex organs of plants and animals
Product	2 cells with identical genetic information	4 sex cells, which may have different genetic information
Chromosome number	full number of chromosomes	

A6 Just before mitosis starts, the chromosomes produce a copy of themselves after which they become shorter and thicker. They then line up across the middle of the cell. The chromosome copies separate, each set going to a new cell (daughter cell). Each daughter cell inherits identical genetic information. Division is complete after the cytoplasm divides and, in plants, when a new cell wall has formed. ❏

Draw arrows between the dividing cells to show the correct sequence. Number the sequence 1 to 5. Colour each chromosome in cell 1 with a different colour. Show what happens to each chromosome during mitosis by using this colour code in the remaining cells.

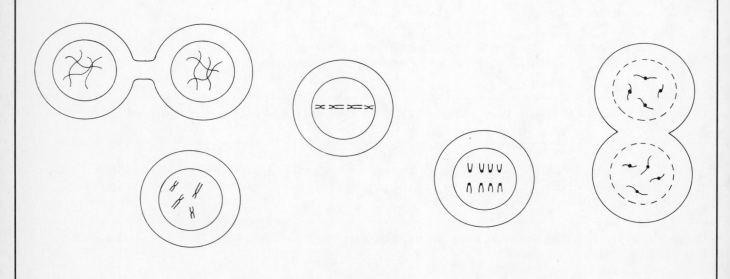

A7 There are two cycles of division in meiosis. In the first division the chromosomes inherited from the female parent pair up with those inherited from the male parent. The chromosome pairs then separate. This results in two cells each with half the original number of chromosomes. The second division of meiosis is just like mitosis – the chromosomes divide, producing four new sex cells each with half the original number of chromosomes. Fertilisation, when sperm and egg fuse, results in a cell with the full chromosome number. ❏

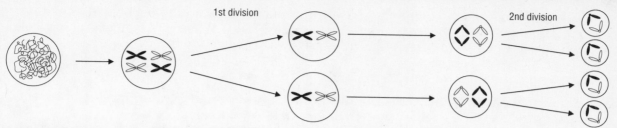

A8 Growth takes place in three stages. First, the number of cells increases by cell division or **mitosis**. Then the cells enlarge, and finally the cells change or **differentiate** to take on particular functions. In humans, growth in the uterus depends on the developing baby receiving food and oxygen from the mother through the **umbilical cord** and across the **placenta**. Waste materials pass in the opposite direction. This maintains the internal environment of the fetus. ❑

B1 Absorption of digested food takes place through the lining of the small intestine. **Villi** increase the surface area of the lining. Only glucose, amino acids, glycerol, water and mineral salts pass into blood capillaries. Fatty acid molecules are too large and are absorbed into **lymph vessels**. ❑

Label the blood capillaries and the lymph vessel.

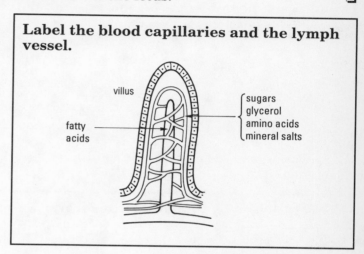

villus

fatty acids

sugars
glycerol
amino acids
mineral salts

B2 The lungs inflate when we inhale and deflate when we exhale because of the action of two sets of muscles – the rib muscles (**intercostals**) and the **diaphragm**. ❑

Write *inhaling* and *exhaling* above the correct descriptions. Label the *intercostal muscles* and the *diaphragm* on the diagram.

....

The intercostal muscles and the diaphragm relax.
The rib-cage falls.
The diaphragm pushes up reducing the volume of the thorax.
Pressure increases and air passes out of the lungs.

Both muscle sets contract.
The rib-cage rises.
The diaphragm pulls down increasing the volume of the thorax.
Pressure in the lungs decreases and air is drawn into the lungs.

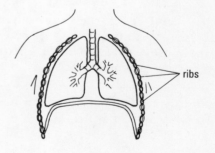

ribs

B3 The structure of the lungs aids gas exchange:

- the air sacs provide a very large surface area for gas exchange
- the air sacs have very thin walls to speed up gas exchange
- the surfaces of the air sacs are moist, which aids the diffusion of gases
- there is a rich blood supply for gases to diffuse into and out of. ❑

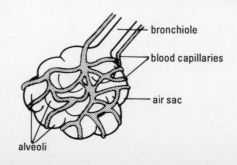

bronchiole

blood capillaries

air sac

alveoli

B4 If you are involved in lengthy or hard exercise your muscles may not be able to get enough oxygen to carry out aerobic respiration. This creates an **oxygen debt**. When you stop exercising you gasp for breath. This takes in extra oxygen needed to repay the oxygen debt. ❏

B5 Co-ordination and control in mammals depends on two systems:
- the **endocrine system**, which uses chemicals called **hormones** to co-ordinate and control long-term changes in the body, such as growth and sexual development
- the **nervous system**, which uses electrical impulses for rapid co-ordination and control of movement. ❏

❏

B6 **Hormones** are used in medicine to treat a wide range of conditions. ❏

Match each hormone to the corresponding treatment. Use a different colour each time.

Hormone	Treatment for
sex hormones	diabetes, control of blood sugar level
growth hormone	promoting human growth
insulin	controlling and promoting fertility

B7 The brain and spinal cord (the central nervous system or CNS) is the co-ordinating centre of the nervous system. ❏

Label the three main parts of the brain.

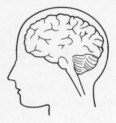

1 **medulla oblongata** – controls involuntary actions, for example, heart rate, breathing, blinking

2 **cerebellum** – co-ordination of movement and balance

3 **cerebrum or cerebral hemispheres** – controls movement and sensations; responsible for memory, thought, feelings

---

B8 In normal situations nerve impulses are transmitted from a sensor along **sensory neurones** to the brain. Responses to this incoming information are made by transmitting an impulse from the CNS along **motor neurones** to an **effector muscle**. The impulse is transmitted across gaps, called **synapses**, between neurones. ❏

Label the synapse in the diagram below. Make a flow diagram to show the path of a nerve impulse from sensor to muscle.

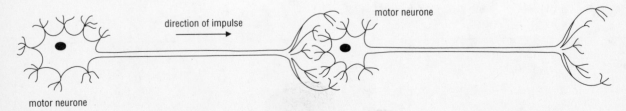

B9 When a reflex action takes place the nerve impulse takes a different, faster, route than normal. This is called the **reflex arc**. The impulse travels to the spinal cord and immediately to a motor neurone and effector muscle rather than transmitting to the brain before starting the response. ❏

> **Give two examples of reflex actions.**

B10 Homeostasis depends on feedback loops to maintain a steady state. They all follow a similar pattern. ❏

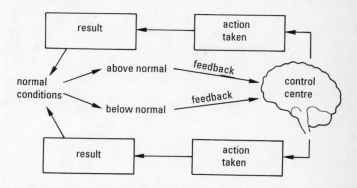

B11 Water balance or **osmoregulation** is controlled by the action of a hormone (produced by the pituitary gland) on the kidneys. When blood water concentration falls, more hormone is produced. This causes additional water to be reabsorbed in the kidney nephrons. ❏

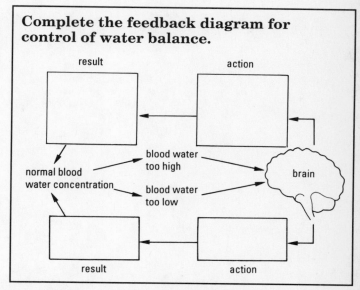

Complete the feedback diagram for control of water balance.

B12 Blood sugar level is controlled by the hormone **insulin**. When blood glucose rises above normal more insulin is produced. This acts on the liver, where excess glucose is removed from the blood and converted to glycogen. If blood glucose falls below normal, insulin production falls and glycogen in the liver is changed back to glucose. ❏

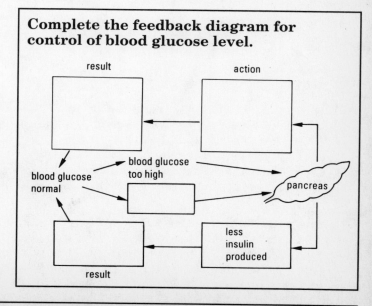

Complete the feedback diagram for control of blood glucose level.

B13 Digested food is transported to the liver where excess **amino acids** are broken down. A product of these reactions is **urea**. This poison is removed from the blood by the kidneys, passed through the ureters to the bladder for storage, and then excreted. Each kidney contains a million filter units called **nephrons**.

Kidney nephrons work in two stages. First, liquid containing urea and other small molecules is forced out of a group of narrow blood capillaries called a **glomerulus** into the capsule of the kidney nephron. This liquid – the glomerular filtrate – contains substances the body cannot afford to lose, in addition to the urea. In the second stage, the valuable substances such as water and mineral salts are reabsorbed into blood capillaries. In this way the kidneys ensure that the composition of the blood stays fairly constant. ❑

Describe what happens at stages 1 and 2 in the kidney nephron.

Stage 1

Stage 2

Label the kidneys, ureter and bladder in the diagram below.

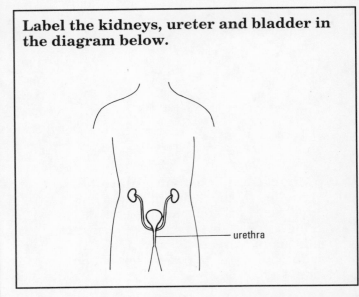

a nephron

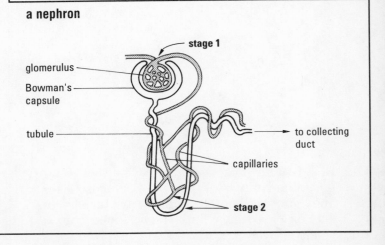

B14 Blood pH depends on the amount of dissolved CO_2 from respiration. CO_2 is an acidic gas. The brain detects any alteration in CO_2 concentration and responds by stimulating the intercostal muscles and diaphragm to alter the breathing rate. ❑

Complete the sentences.

When blood pH falls the breathing rate ....

When blood pH rises the breathing rate ....

B15 The maintenance of body temperature in mammals depends on **metabolism** (the body's chemistry) to generate heat. Most heat is generated from respiration in the muscles and liver. Special cells in the brain detect changes in blood temperature and the brain responds to these changes in a number of ways. The responses to an increase in blood temperature are the opposite to the responses to a decrease in blood temperature.

When it is too cold:

- the thyroid is stimulated to increase the metabolic rate of cells
- shivering begins
- blood is diverted away from the skin surface
- body hairs are raised by the contraction of hair muscles
- sweating stops.

❏

What happens when it is too hot?

C1 Plants take water into their root hair cells by **osmosis**. The same process transfers water across the root cells to the **xylem** tissue, which transports water up the stem. ❏

Draw an arrow on diagram 1 to show the direction of flow of water. Label this *osmosis*. Explain how water now moves from the root hair cell into cell 1 as shown in diagram 2.

Diagram 1: water moves into root hair cells by osmosis.

Diagram 2

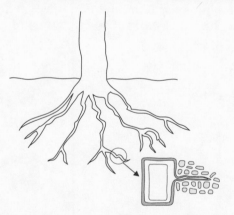

xylem

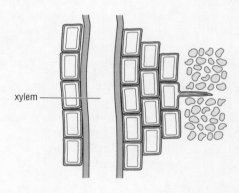

The water concentration in the cell sap of root hair cells is lower than the water concentration in the surrounding soil. Water therefore enters the root hair cells by osmosis.

C2 Water and dissolved mineral salts enter the dead xylem tissue by diffusion. Water is drawn up the stem by the pull of **transpiration** from the surface of leaves. ❏

C3 Substances required for growth and reproduction are transported in living **phloem** vessels. These are found towards the outside of the stem or just under the bark of trees. Substances move into and out of the phloem by **active transport**. ❏

D1 Genetic variation can arise in a number of ways:

- sexual reproduction, which produces offspring with a combination of genes from both parents
- meiosis, which shuffles genes into new combinations, resulting in variation between sex cells
- mutations, which alter the genetic material. ❏

D2 In meiosis, variation results from the way in which the paired chromosomes line up at the first division ❏

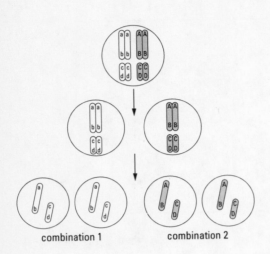

combination 1   combination 2

Complete the diagram by showing two more possible chromosome combinations.

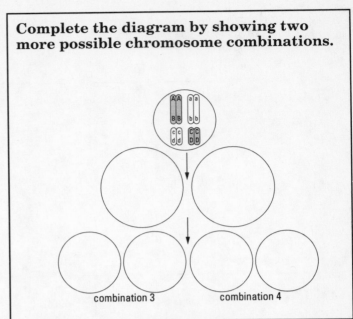

combination 3   combination 4

D3 Mutations can be caused by radiation or certain chemicals, and also occur naturally. Mutations are random and are only passed on to the next generation if they affect the sex cells. Mutations can affect a whole chromosome or a small part of a single gene. For example, the condition Down's syndrome in humans is caused by a mutation that produces one extra chromosome. Sickle-cell anaemia, however, results from a small mutation within the gene for haemoglobin – the red pigment responsible for carrying oxygen in red blood cells. This can reduce the efficiency of oxygen transport. ❏

D4 Some diseases can be inherited:

- sickle-cell anaemia
- cystic fibrosis
- haemophilia. ❏

D5 The study of genetics allows us to predict the pattern of inheritance of a characteristic determined by a single gene, for example tongue rolling in humans. There are four basic rules:

1 We inherit one gene from each parent for this characteristic. A pair of genes for the same characteristic are called **alleles**.
2 All body cells carry two alleles for tongue rolling, but sex cells (as a result of meiosis) carry only one allele for tongue rolling.
3 There can be two forms of an allele – a **dominant** allele and a **recessive** allele. Alleles are normally shown as letters – a capital letter for dominant (T for tongue rolling) and a small letter for recessive (t for non-tongue rolling).
4 Any individual can have one of three combinations of alleles:

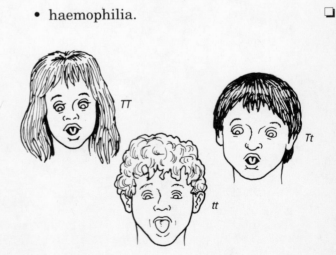

- 2 dominant alleles (*TT*) – a tongue roller (**homozygous dominant**)
- 1 dominant and 1 recessive allele (*Tt*) – a tongue roller (**heterozygous**)
- 2 recessive alleles (*tt*) – a non-tongue roller (**homozygous recessive**). ❏

D6 The results of a cross (or mating) can be shown using letters to describe the alleles, for example, in these crosses between fruit flies (*Drosophila*): ❏

1 A fly with straight wings **phenotype** (physical appearance) and *SS* **genotype** (2 dominant alleles) is crossed with a fly with curly wings phenotype (*ss* genotype).

	male parent	×	**female parent**
genotype of parents	*SS*		*ss*
genotype of sex cells	all *S*		all *s*
genotype of offspring		all *Ss*	
phenotype of offspring		all with straight wings	

2

	male parent	×	**female parent**
genotype of parents	*Ss*		*Ss*
genotype of sex cells	*S* or *s*		*S* or *s*

genotype of offspring   *SS* *Ss* *Ss* *ss*

phenotypic ratio   3 straight wings : 1 curly wings

genotypic ratio   1   2   1

homozygous dominant : heterozygous : homozygous recessive

Show the results of the cross below. Give both the *phenotypic* and *genotypic* ratios in the offspring.

male *Ss* × *ss* female

curly winged
fruit fly (*ss*)

D7 Chromosomes are made up of many genes, which are made of the chemical **DNA**, **d**eoxyribo**n**ucleic **a**cid. The DNA molecule is a double helix (double spiral).

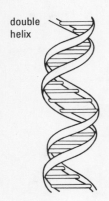

double helix

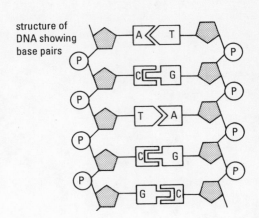

structure of DNA showing base pairs

D8 There are four bases in the DNA molecule and these can only pair in two ways to make the cross-links. They are usually shown by using their first letters. **C** always pairs with **G**, and **T** always pairs with **A**.

D9 Most cells in an organism contain all the chromosomes. For example, all human cells contain 46 chromosomes except the sex cells, which contain half this number. When a cell divides the DNA must be copied (replicated) to ensure that the 'daughter' cells contain the complete set of chromosomes.

Complete the diagram by writing the letters of the correct bases in the empty spaces.

Stages of DNA replication

1	DNA double helix unwinds
2	Bonds between bases break
3	Matching bases joined to sugar and phosphate molecules build a new parallel strand
4	Two identical DNA molecules are formed

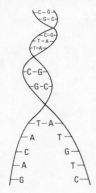
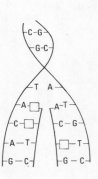
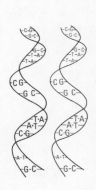

D10 A gene is a section of DNA and has a unique sequence of bases. The bases are a code for the production of a particular protein. This protein allows the inherited characteristic to develop. For example:

gene   → production of protein   → development of characteristic   → characteristic

brown eye colour   particular enzyme produced   enzyme controls formation of brown   brown eyes
in iris cells   pigment in iris cells

D11 DNA is in the nucleus of the cell but protein synthesis (production) takes place in the cytoplasm. A messenger molecule takes the genetic code from the nucleus to the cytoplasm. The messenger code is read in groups of three bases called **triplets**. Each triplet attracts a particular amino acid. The protein is built up amino acid by amino acid, and the order depends on the order of triplets on the DNA. When the complete message has been read (translated) the protein is complete and can carry out its function.

48

Label the following on the diagram: *DNA, protein, messenger molecule, amino acid, triplets.*

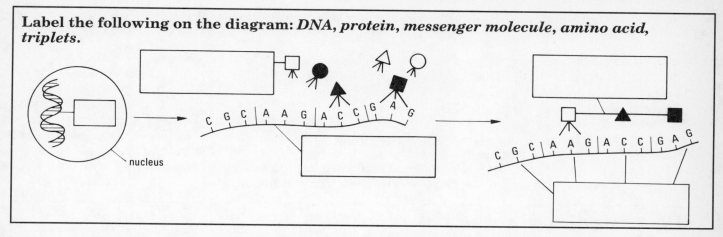

D12 Our knowledge of genetics has been used in the **selective breeding** of varieties of plants and animals that have desirable characteristics. This is also called artificial selection. For example, wild forms of wheat have been crossed with cultivated wheat to produce new varieties that give a bigger yield and have better resistance to disease. ❏

Describe two other examples of selective breeding.

D13 It can be an advantage to produce **clones** – individuals that are genetically identical – by **asexual reproduction**. Many fruit plants are clones grown from cuttings, and the grower can rely on obtaining the desired product from every tree. Cloning avoids sexual reproduction, which would introduce variation into the offspring. Soon animals will be cloned on a commercial scale. ❏

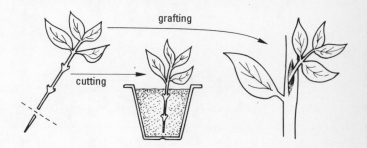

D14 Understanding genetics at the molecular level has led to the development of genetic engineering – a form of **biotechnology**. Genetic engineering involves inserting a fragment of DNA containing one or more genes from one organism into the DNA of another organism, usually a bacterium. When the bacterium divides the altered DNA is passed to both daughter cells, and each individual makes the protein coded for by the inserted gene. The bacteria soon produce a very large population of clones from which the protein can be collected and purified. Human insulin is now produced in this way. ❏

D15 In the future, it may be possible to alter genes in a fertilised egg by introducing those that would

Label the following on the diagram: *bacterial DNA, clones, extraction and purification, human insulin gene.*

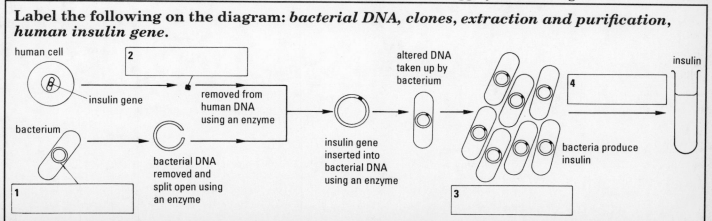

produce more desirable characteristics or by replacing undesirable disease-causing genes. This has serious social and ethical implications. Genetic engineers work to a strict code of practice. ❑

D16 Variation between individuals of the same species is the starting point of **evolution**. In any population some individuals are better adapted to their environment than others. **Natural selection** ensures that the fittest survive and reproduce. In this way the species survives even if environmental conditions change. The peppered moth is a good example. Natural selection works in favour of moths that are well camouflaged against the bark of trees. Before the industrial revolution peppered moths with a speckled colouring had the best chance of avoiding predators as they couldn't be seen on lichen-covered tree trunks. Then tree trunks in industrial areas became blackened by factory smoke, and darker coloured moths were, and still are, selected for. ❑

E1 The **biosphere** is made up of the Earth's crust and surrounding atmosphere along with all the

Use the words below to complete the flow chart.

against   darker   for

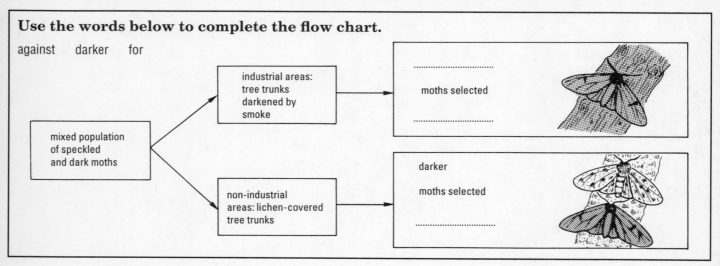

living organisms present. The main parts of the biosphere are interdependent. Human activity can have a harmful effect on the biosphere. ❑

E2 Economic demands can lead to the poor management of ecosystems. For example, the need to

For each human activity, draw lines to match each effect with the correct part of the biosphere affected.

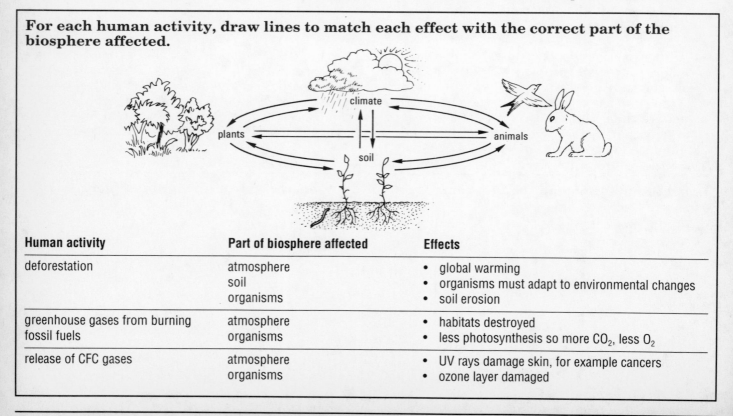

Human activity	Part of biosphere affected	Effects
deforestation	atmosphere soil organisms	• global warming • organisms must adapt to environmental changes • soil erosion
greenhouse gases from burning fossil fuels	atmosphere organisms	• habitats destroyed • less photosynthesis so more CO_2, less O_2
release of CFC gases	atmosphere organisms	• UV rays damage skin, for example cancers • ozone layer damaged

produce more food can lead to **desertification**.

❑

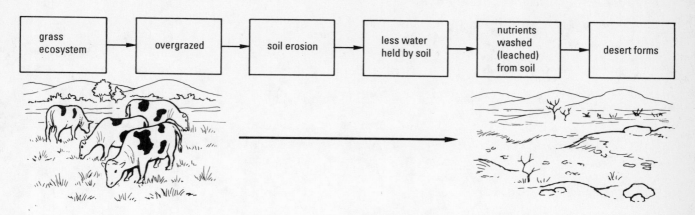

E3 Materials for growth and energy are transferred through ecosystems by food chains and webs and by recycling, which involves decomposers. These processes are not very efficient and minerals and other nutrients can be lost by **leaching** (being washed from the soil by rain).

❑

E4 Energy is dissipated at every link in a food chain, and very little ends up being used for growth of the next organism in the chain. Energy is wasted as heat from respiration and as movement. Uneaten and excreted material can be wasted when it is not recycled by decomposers. Within a food web there are various levels.

❑

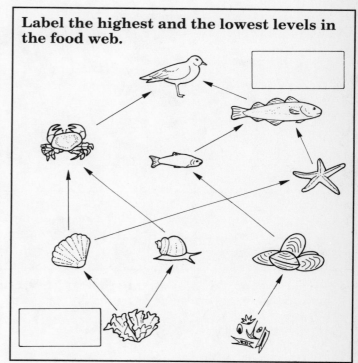

Label the highest and the lowest levels in the food web.

E5 The nitrogen and carbon cycles maintain the balance of these elements in an ecosystem. Other elements such as phosphorus (required for the genetic material DNA and for energy-storing chemicals) are also cycled.

❑

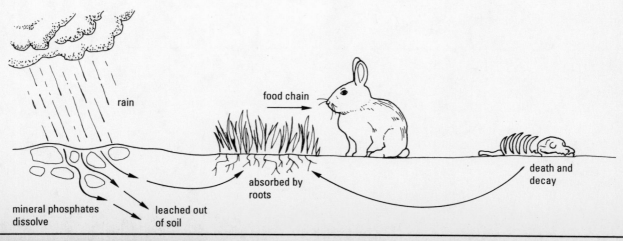

E6 In the nitrogen cycle, there are two groups of bacteria that help make nitrogen in the soil available to plants in the form of soluble nitrates:

- **nitrogen-fixing bacteria** in the soil change atmospheric nitrogen directly into nitrates. The roots of some plants (for example, peas, beans and lupins) contain nitrogen-fixing bacteria
- microbes produce nitrogen-containing ammonia from the decomposition of dead plant and animal material. Ammonia is changed to nitrites then nitrates by **nitrifying bacteria**.

The soil may also contain **de-nitrifying bacteria** that deplete the soil of nitrates and return nitrogen to the air.

Label the *nitrogen-fixing bacteria*, *nitrifying bacteria* and *de-nitrifying bacteria* in the diagram below.

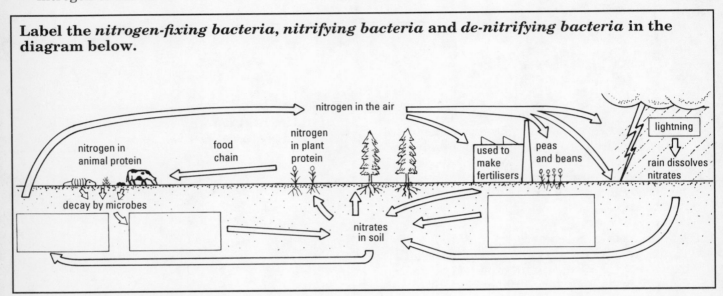

E7 As the human population grows, more and more food is required. Ecosystems must be managed carefully to reduce energy wastage and maximise crop yields. Management must be sensitive so that ecosystems are not damaged.

Draw lines to match each danger to the correct agricultural process for maximising yield. Use a different colour each time.

Crop yield maximised by

removing hedges to increase area of fields, making ploughing and harvesting easier

adding fertilisers to the soil

using insecticides to kill pests

growing same plants in huge areas (monoculture)

Dangers to be avoided

rapid spread of disease or pests

destruction of habitats

fertilisers leached from soil into waterways causing pollution

poisons pass into food chains and are concentrated along chain

---

ATTAINMENT TARGET 3 (Sc3)

Materials and their properties

BIG IDEAS

A There are different types of substance with different properties. These properties depend on the structure of the substance which in turn depends on the interactions between its atoms.

B Substances can be changed by physical actions, geological actions or chemical reactions. People can change substances in raw materials (like oil, rocks and air) into useful products. Symbols can be used to show these and other reactions.

C Chemical reactions show patterns. You can make predictions from patterns like the Periodic Table and the reactivity series of metals.

A1 The five main groups of material (ceramic, metal, plastic, glass and fibre) have been used to manufacture this house. Draw lines to match each of the useful properties to at least one material.
❏

fibre insulation

plastic gutter

glass window

aluminium frame

steel bar in lintel

brick wall

concrete step

Properties

| high tensile strength |
| high compressive strength |
| low porosity |
| low thermal conductivity |
| high thermal stability |
| low cost |

A2 Materials are composed of substances and can be grouped (classified) into **solids**, **liquids** and **gases**. Different types of materials have different **properties**.

Solids
- stay where they are put
- stay the same shape

Liquids
- flow over the surface
- change shape, form puddles

Gases
- flow everywhere
- change shape, fill space ❏

Under normal living conditions		
three solids are:	**three liquids are:**	**three gases are:**
• metal	• petrol	• air
•	•	• ....
•	•	• ....

A3 The **particles** are arranged differently in a solid, a liquid and a gas. ❏

Use particle drawings to illustrate the different properties of ice, water and water vapour.

Ice has a fixed shape because the particles are held together strongly.

Water changes shape because the particles are held more loosely and can move about, sliding over one another.

Water vapour spreads because the particles are separate and move quickly.

A4 The **state** of a substance changes with temperature.

solid gold → liquid gold → gaseous gold
at 20 °C   at 1064 °C   at 2807 °C

solid water	→	liquid water	→	gaseous water
at −5 °C		above .... °C		above .... °C

A5 A substance's properties change when its state changes. The **water cycle** is a good example to illustrate this.

Draw a diagram to show how water can move from sea to clouds to snow to river, and to sea again. Add these labels to your diagram:

heating   evaporation   condensation   wind   freezing   melting   flowing   river

A6 All particles of matter have kinetic energy, including single atoms, molecules and networks. Particles move about, which is why you can smell perfume in all parts of a room. The particles **diffuse** through the air to your nose, moving from an area of high concentration to one of low concentration. Brownian motion provides indirect evidence for this.

A7 When a substance is heated, its particles move about more. The spaces between them increase and the substance **expands** (gets bigger). Eventually it **changes state**; a solid melts and finally the liquid vaporises. These steps all require energy, and are shown in the diagram below, going from left to right.

Write one word to describe each step in the reverse process, going from right to left.

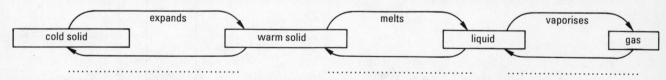

cold solid — expands — warm solid — melts — liquid — vaporises — gas

....

A8 Elements are special substances; they make up all other substances. An element contains one kind of atom. Each atom is made from three types of particle.

Draw arrows from the labels to the correct part of the drawing.

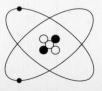

nucleus

proton (mass 1, charge +)

neutron (mass 1, charge 0)

electron (mass very small, charge −)

A9 The nucleus contains protons.

atomic number (Z) = number of protons

In a **neutral** atom, number of protons = number of electrons.   ❏

Calculate the numbers of protons and electrons in each example.

$_3$Li $_6$C $_{11}$Na $_{12}$Mg $_{17}$Cl

3 protons (+++)   .... protons   .... protons   .... protons   .... protons

3 electrons (– – –)   .... electrons   .... electrons   .... electrons   .... electrons

---

A10 The nucleus also contains neutrons.

mass number (A) = protons + neutrons

For example, this atom has:

- 3 protons (atomic number)
- 3 electrons (neutral atom)
- 4 neutrons (mass number minus atomic number).   ❏

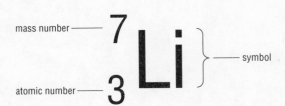

mass number ——— 7

atomic number ——— 3 **Li** } ——— symbol

Complete the table for each of these examples.

Symbol	Number of protons	Number of electrons	Number of neutrons
$_{13}^{27}$Al			
$_{9}^{19}$F			
$_{79}^{197}$Au			

A11 Isotopes are atoms of the same element (*same atomic number*) but which have different numbers of neutrons (*different mass number*). For example, ^{35}Cl and ^{37}Cl have 17 protons each. Therefore the first isotope has $(35 - 17)$ neutrons; the second has $(37 - 17)$ neutrons.   ❏

Work out the numbers of protons, neutrons and electrons in these two isotopes of carbon.

^{12}C $p =$ .... $n =$ .... $e =$ ....

^{14}C $p =$ .... $n =$ .... $e =$ ....

A12 The electrons are arranged around the nucleus in energy levels, called **electron shells**. For elements 1–20, the first level holds only 2 electrons, the second 8, the third 8, and so on.   ❏

Which electron shell determines the chemical behaviour of an atom?
Add the missing labels on the diagram.

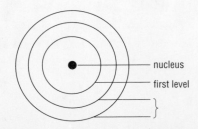

nucleus

first level

A13 An atom can lose or gain electrons and become a charged **ion**. For example, the Li atom has 3 electrons; the Li^+ ion has only 2 electrons: +++ (3 positive protons), −− (cancelled by only 2 negative electrons). ❏

A14 Atoms join together to achieve a stable, full outer electron shell. Sodium has to lose 1 electron to do so and its combining power (or **valency**) is therefore 1. Carbon has to share 4 electrons and its valency is therefore 4. Valency is related to group number. ❏

Work out how many electrons each ion has.			
	$_{11}Na^+$	$_{12}Mg^{2+}$	$_9F^-$	$_8O^{2-}$
protons	....	....	....	....
electrons	....	....	....	....
overall charge	+	2+	−	2−

Complete the gaps in this summary table.

Group	1	2				6	7	8
Valency	1	2	3	4	3	2		

A15 Elements join together to form **compounds**. The name of the compound indicates which elements are present in it. Copper nitr**ide** is made from copper and nitrogen **only**. Copper nitr**ate** is made from copper, nitrogen **and** oxygen. Carbon **di**oxide is made from carbon and **two** oxygens. Sulphur **tri**oxide is made from sulphur and **three** oxygens. ❏

Carbon tetrachloride is made from .... and .... chlorines.

Sodium chlorate is made from .... and .... and ....

.... is made from copper, sulphur and oxygen.

A16 The formula of a compound can be worked out by using valency pictures. ❏

Example	**Complete**	**Complete**

Compound Calcium chloride | **Compound** Sodium oxide | **Compound**

Formula $CaCl_2$ | **Formula** | **Formula**

A17 Compounds that are made from metal joined to non-metal are **ionic**. Compounds that are made from non-metal and non-metal are **covalent**. Metals joined to other metals are called alloys. ❏

> **Use one colour to underline all the ionic compounds in A15 on page 57. Use another colour to underline all the covalent compounds. Add a colour key.**

A18 Ionic compounds have high melting points and are therefore solids at room temperature. They conduct electricity when molten or dissolved in water. ❏

> Covalent compounds have .... melting points and are therefore often liquids or gases at room temperature.
>
> With electricity, they .... These properties can be used to separate compounds of different types.

B1 Oil and natural gas formed millions of years ago from the remains of tiny sea creatures. The fossil fuels were then trapped between layers of non-porous rock until people discovered how to extract them. ❏

> **Add the following labels to explain the diagrams.**
>
> millions of years later   decaying sea creatures   sand and mud   heat and pressure   rock   fossil fuel   drilling rig
>
>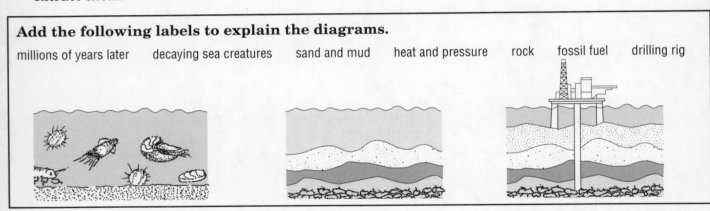

B2 Hydrocarbons are covalent compounds. Crude oil is a mixture of hydrocarbons. It is changed into useful products by the following processes.

- The mixture of hydrocarbons is **distilled**. Smaller hydrocarbons boil and condense at lower temperatures than larger hydrocarbons. Fractions with small molecules burn well and are in great demand as fuels. Those with larger molecules are not as useful.
- There is too much of some of the heavy fractions. Their molecules are **cracked** (using heat and a catalyst) to make smaller molecules. Some of these are unsaturated.
- The unsaturated molecules are **polymerised** to make big molecules.
- Some molecules are **reformed** to change their structures. ❏

> **The processes described above are shown in the diagram. Add the following names to it:**
>
> distillation   cracking   polymerisation   reforming
>
>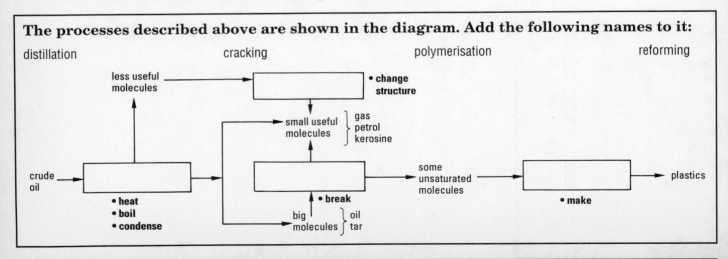

B3 Some of the products from the fractional distillation of crude oil are used as fuels. ❏

List three examples.

B4 When hydrocarbons burn completely, they produce water and carbon dioxide:

$$CH_4 + 2O_2 \rightarrow 2H_2O + CO_2$$

Larger hydrocarbon molecules cannot get enough oxygen to burn completely and therefore they often produce carbon (soot) and/or carbon monoxide (CO). ❏

B5 The combustion of hydrocarbons, for example petrol in car engines, is a major source of air pollution. ❏

Draw lines to match the pollutants formed in a car engine with possible effects on the environment.

Pollutant	Possible effect
CO_2	acid rain
CO	brain damage
NO_2	greenhouse gas
lead compounds	poisonous

B6 There are different families of hydrocarbons; for example the alkanes and the alkenes.

and and are alkanes

Alkanes are saturated hydrocarbons because they have single C—C covalent bonds. ❏

Complete the following:

and   and   are alkenes

Alkenes are unsaturated hydrocarbons because they have ....

B7 There are chemical patterns that enable us to predict the form of reaction and its associated energy changes. The table below shows the pattern of reactivity of the common metals with water, acid and chlorine. The amount of energy released in a reaction can indicate the relative reactivity of the metal. ❏

Use one colour to highlight the blocks of reactions that give out a lot of energy, another colour for those that give out some energy and a different colour for those that do not release any energy. Complete the final column as fully as you can.

	with water	with acid	with chlorine	with oxygen
K Na Li Ca Mg	displace hydrogen gas from cold water	violent explosive reaction	combine very energetically with chlorine to form stable ionic chloride salts	
Al Zn Fe Sn	only displace hydrogen from steam	displace hydrogen from acid		
Pb Cu Hg Au Pt	do not displace hydrogen from water or steam	do not displace hydrogen from acid	combine quickly to form stable salts / combine slowly to form unstable salts	

colour key

☐ give out a lot of energy   ☐ give out some energy   ☐ do not release any energy

B8 Reactive metals give out a lot of energy when they react and they form **stable** compounds. Unreactive metals form unstable compounds that break up easily, needing only a little energy to do so. ❏

B9 Our supply of metals is **finite**, which means it will not last forever. Used metal should therefore be **recycled**. ❏

B10 Although their reactivity varies, metals have many similar chemical properties. For example, they react with non-metals to form positive ions, they mix with other metals to form alloys and most corrode in the presence of oxygen and water. ❏

B11 Metals are extracted from metal compounds called **ores** that are found in the Earth. The more reactive the metal, the more stable its ore. For example, copper can be **extracted** from its ore simply by heating (or using chemical methods) whereas iron ore needs to be heated with carbon to extract iron. To make aluminium, the aluminium ore (bauxite) must be melted and then electrolysed. ❏

Use the facts given above to help you complete the summary of how metals are extracted.

Metals	Extracted from ore by
K, Na, Li, Ca, Mg, Al	
Zn, Fe, Sn, Pb	
Cu, Hg	
Ag, Pt, Au	

B12 A metal can **displace** (push out) from solution any other metal that is below it in the reactivity series. This can be used to obtain the pure metal from a compound. ❑

> **When nickel is added to a solution of copper chloride, brown copper metal is formed. Nothing happens when copper is added to nickel chloride solution. However, nickel is formed when iron is added to the nickel chloride solution.**
>
> **Write the three metals in order of increasing reactivity.**
>
> ....

B13 Metals are shiny and easy to reshape. They are often hard, strong and quite dense. They **conduct** electricity and also heat. ❑

> **Use the Periodic Table to predict the results of the experiment below.**
>
> | Element | Does the bulb light? |
> |---------|----------------------|
> | copper | |
> | magnesium | |
> | sulphur | |
> | Ag | |
> | Ar | |
> | Al | |
>
> experiment
>
>
> bulb
>
> element

B14 Most metal elements have various physical properties in common. ❑

> **Use a dictionary to find the meanings of these typical metal properties.**
>
> malleable ....
>
> ....
>
> ....
>
> ductile ....
>
> ....
>
> ....
>
> high tensile strength ....
>
> ....
>
> ....

B15 Industry uses a wide variety of chemical processes to manufacture materials. Any chemical process should be **evaluated**, using a range of scientific information, for its effect on people and the environment, in addition to considering its economic importance. ❑

B16 A **material** is composed of matter. It is often a substance that is useful to people because it can be changed into an object. The object is **manufactured** from **raw materials** (found in the Earth, sea, air and living things). This process costs time, energy and money. It may also have an environmental cost.

These ideas are shown in the spider diagram below.

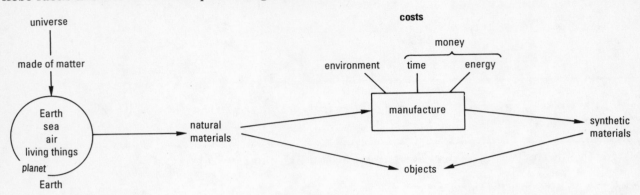

> **List five objects that are made from rocks and minerals.**

B17 Materials can be **classified** in various ways, for example natural/synthetic or cheap/expensive. If they are divided according to properties then five main groups emerge:

- metals
- plastics
- fibres
- glasses
- ceramics.

Complete the table below by adding two examples of each group.

Group	Source	Main properties	Your two examples
metals	ores in the ground	conduct well; easily shaped; strong	
glasses	made from rocks (sand, limestone)	transparent; brittle; unreactive	
plastics	made from oil	insulators; easily shaped; long-lasting	
ceramics	made from clay	hard; high melting points; unreactive	
fibres	natural (synthetic from oil)	form long, thin strands; flexible; strong	

B18 The valency or combining power of **transition elements** is variable. In a compound, the valency of the metal atom is given as a Roman numeral after its name, for example, copper(II) chloride and copper(I) chloride.

> **Tick the diagram that shows the valency picture for copper(I) chloride.**
>
>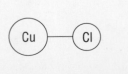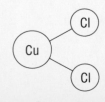

B19 Some ionic compounds contain **groups** of atoms that act like a single unit. The formulae and valencies of the most common groups are given below.

Valency	1	2	3
	ammonium, NH$_4$	sulphate, SO$_4$	phosphate, PO$_4$
Group	hydroxide, OH	carbonate, CO$_3$	
	nitrate, NO$_3$		

B20 Valency pictures can be used to work out the formulae of substances with groups.

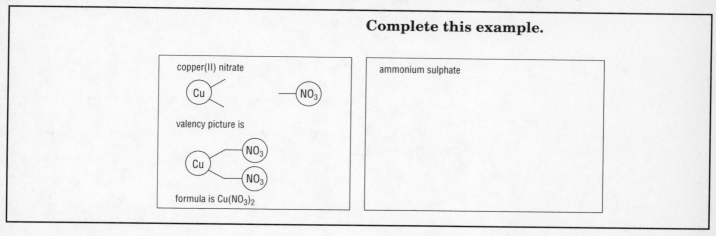

Complete this example.

ammonium sulphate

B21 Chemical formulae are a short-hand way of describing substances. To work out a **chemical formula**, follow these rules.

1 Write down the name of the substance.
2 Look up the symbols for the elements/groups.
3 Write the valency of each atom/group.
4 If they don't balance, swap the valancies.
5 Draw a valency picture if you need some help.

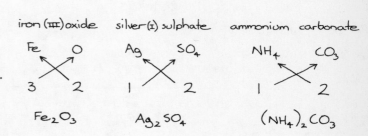

Write the formulae for the following substances, laying out your working in the same way as shown above.

sodium oxide   hydrogen fluoride   magnesium chloride   silver(I) sulphide   iron(II) chloride

lithium nitrate   aluminium phosphate   calcium hydroxide   ammonium carbonate

B22 Covalent compounds often have names that describe their formula: carbon **di**oxide is CO_2 and carbon **mon**oxide is CO; sulphur **di**oxide is SO_2 and sulphur **tri**oxide is SO_3. ❏

B23 During combustion, the particles join with oxygen to form compounds called **oxides**.

hydrogen + oxygen → hydrogen oxide (water)

$$2H_2 + O_2 \rightarrow 2H_2O$$

carbon + oxygen → carbon dioxide

$$C + O_2 \rightarrow CO_2$$ ❏

Complete the following word equations:

copper + oxygen → ....

.... + oxygen → sulphur dioxide

.... + ... → calcium oxide

methane + oxygen → .... + ...
  (CH_4)

ethanol + ... → water + ...
  (C_2H_6O)

B24 A **chemical equation** is a precise description of a chemical reaction. It can be built up in steps.

1 Write the equation in words.
2 Put it into symbols, using the correct formulae.
3 Add arithmetic symbols and balance by multiplying the formulae.
4 Include the state symbols.

Remember:

• never change the correct formula to balance the equation
• state symbols are (s) = solid, (l) = liquid, (g) = gas, (aq) = aqueous solution. ❏

1, iron + chlorine ⟶ iron (III) chloride

2, Fe Cl_2 $FeCl_3$

3, $2Fe + 3Cl_2$ ⟶ $2FeCl_3$

4, $2Fe_{(s)} + 3Cl_{2(g)}$ ⟶ $2FeCl_{3(s)}$

Use the rules above to write equations for:

the **neutralisation** of hydrochloric acid by calcium carbonate

the extraction of copper from copper oxide by **reduction** with carbon

the **combustion** of methane

B25 Rain, snow, ice and wind all affect the materials on the Earth. **Weathering** of rock causes **erosion** of the land. Mountains are eventually worn away by water and by changing temperature. The process of weathering and erosion occurs as follows:

a) heat from the Sun causes cracks to develop
b) water gets into the cracks

---

c) water freezes and cracks widen
d) rock breaks
e) bits of rock are washed away by rainwater
f) rock fragments are transported away to form sediments and soils.

This diagram of weathering and erosion is not complete. Read the sequence in B25 and then complete the diagram by drawing in the missing parts.

a)   b)   c)   d)

e)   f)

B26 A **mineral** is a single substance. A rock is usually a mixture of different minerals. The minerals in a rock can be identified by using chemical tests and by measuring physical properties like hardness and density.

Underline the minerals in this list:

calcite   marble   rock salt   basalt   fluorite   iron pyrites

B27 The structure of a rock indicates how it was formed.

• **Igneous** rocks contain crystals that have formed as the molten rock (magma) cooled. The crystals may be small, as in basalt, or, if the molten rock cooled more slowly, they may be large, as in granite. Pumice and similar rocks even contain bubbles left by escaping gas.
• **Sedimentary** rocks are often layered because the fragments of mineral that make up the rock settled out from moving water. Shale contains very small fragments, sandstone is made of bigger ones and conglomerate has fragments as big as stones in it.
• **Metamorphic** rocks are usually hard and may contain unusual minerals. They were formed by the action of great heat and pressure on existing rocks.

Rocks are often hundreds of millions of years old: a piece of sandstone, for example, might have been formed 185 000 000 years ago.

Give two examples of each rock type below:

Igneous	Sedimentary	Metamorphic
....	....	....
....	....	....

The diagram below shows part of the rock cycle. Add the following labels.

volcanic eruption   weathering and erosion   magma   igneous rock   sedimentary rock   metamorphic rock

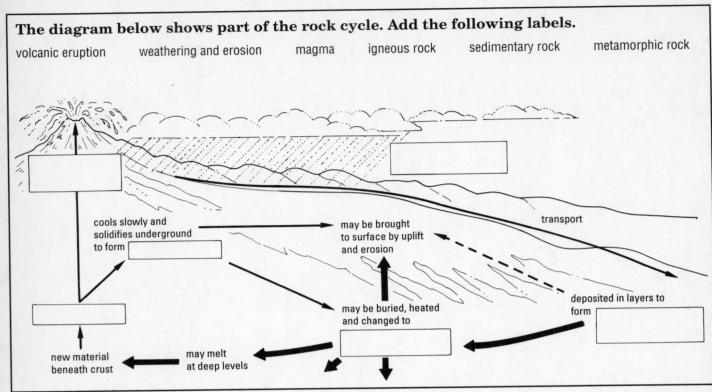

B28 Explain how each of the following three rock types was formed, using some of the words below to help you.

molten   cooled   quickly   slowly   creatures   heated   metamorphic   sedimentary   igneous

limestone containing many tiny fossilised shells

granite with unusually large crystals

marble containing limestone minerals but not shells

B29 Most of the valuable materials on Earth are present as part of a thin layer of rock on the surface of the Earth. The five most abundant elements are O (47%), Si (28%), Al (8%), Fe (5%), Ca (4%).

Draw a bar chart to show this data.

C1 All materials are built from **elements**, which are substances that cannot be broken down into simpler substances. The Periodic Table of elements has **metals** on the left-hand side and **non-metals** on the right, arranged in order of ascending atomic number.

On the Periodic Table below, draw a dividing line between metals and non-metals. Then, colour all the elements that are gases at room temperature. Use a different colour to identify the two elements that are liquid at room temperature (bromine and mercury). Use two more colours to identify the most common non-metal and most common metal in the Earth's crust. Add a colour key.

colour key

H																	He
Li	Be											B	C	N	O	F	Ne
Na	Mg											Al	Si	P	S	Cl	Ar
K	Ca	Sc	Ti	V	Cr	Mn	Fe	Co	Ni	Cu	Zn	Ga	Ge	As	Se	Br	Kr
Rb	Sr	Y	Zr	Nb	Mo	Tc	Ru	Rh	Pd	Ag	Cd	In	Sn	Sb	Te	I	Xe
Cs	Ba		Hf	Ta	W	Re	Os	Ir	Pt	Au	Hg	Tl	Pb	Bi	Po	At	Rn
Fr	Ra		Unq	Unp													

C2 The 92 natural elements are placed in different **groups** in the Periodic Table. The elements in each group are chemically similar, though there is a gradual change from top to bottom of the group. For example Group 1, the alkali metals, are all very reactive metals but Li is less reactive than Na, which is less reactive than K. Group 8, the rare gases, are all very unreactive non-metal gases at room temperature, though the density of the gases increases down the group. ❏

On the outline of the Periodic Table below, label the following:

all groups, 1–8   the reactive metals   the transition metals   the noble gases   the halogens   a period

C3 There are **trends** within the groups of the Periodic Table. In Group 1, the melting points decrease as we descend the group. The metals become softer and the reactions become more energetic. The chemical behaviour of the elements remains similar, however, because they contain similar atoms. ❏

C4 There are also some gradual changes in the properties of the elements as you descend Group 7. ❏

Complete the profiles below to show some of the differences in the Group 7 elements.

Element	Colour	Density	Reactivity	Displacement	Uses
F					water, toothpaste
Cl					bleach, pesticides
Br					film, petrol additive
I					antiseptic, film

C5 There is always a pattern of gradual change down a group. ❏

Complete the table by writing in the names and colours of the elements that are being described.

Element	Colour	Density (g/cm³)	Reactivity	Uses
a)		0.15	very unreactive	airships, aircraft tyres
b)		1.20	very unreactive	fill discharge lamps
c)		1.38	very unreactive	fill electric light bulbs
d)		2.15	very unreactive	fill discharge tubes
e)		2.94	very unreactive	fill strobe lamps
f)		4.40	unreactive, radioactive	health hazard

C6 There are also trends in physical and chemical properties across each period of the table. This is called **periodicity**. For example, the size of the atoms decreases from Li to F and from Na to Cl. ❏

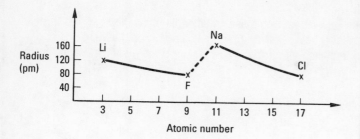

Complete the diagram to show the periodic change in melting point of the elements from Na to Cl.

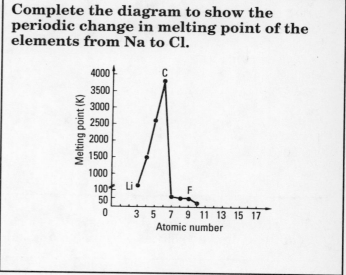

C7 The metals in Group 1 are so reactive that they have to be stored under oil to keep them away from oxygen and damp. For example potassium is so reactive that it bursts into flames in water. The word equation for this chemical reaction is: ❏

alkali metal + water → metal hydroxide + hydrogen

Complete the word equations for other reactions of the alkali metals.

1 Alkali metal + oxygen →

2 Alkali metal + chlorine →

C8 Metals react with oxygen to form **basic oxides**. These are alkaline if they dissolve (like Group 1 metal oxides) and neutral if they do not (like the transition metal oxides). Non-metal oxides are acidic. ❏

Label the main blocks of oxides in the table as *alkaline, neutral* or *acidic.*

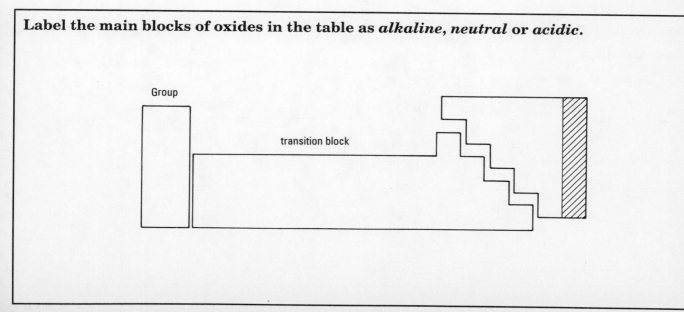

C9 You can identify elements by the ways in which they react.

Read the passage and then name the elements that are described.

Element A is a greenish poisonous gas whereas element B is a pale yellow gas. Both gases react violently with sodium to form a white powder, which is ionic. The two elements are similar to element C because they are in the same group. Element C is a poisonous non-metal that has a valency of 1. It is a reasonably good bleach, but not as good as A or B. Element B can displace A and C from their compounds.

Element A is ....

Element B is ....

Element C is ....

The group name is ....

C10 The **chlor-alkali industry** uses salt as a raw material. Salt solution is electrolysed to produce sodium hydroxide solution, hydrogen and chlorine.

Label the diagram of the membrane electrolysis cell to show where the three products form.

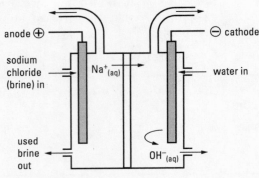

C11 The three products of the chlor-alkali process are sold to other companies who use them to make a variety of useful materials.

From your knowledge of the chlor-alkali process, complete the table below.

Raw materials: salt, water

Cost of process: electricity, ...

Product	Sold to make	Benefits	Drawbacks
	pesticides PVC bleach clean water		
	margarine hydrochloric acid		
	paper soaps/detergents synthetic materials		

C12 Transition metals are placed on the Periodic Table in a block between the main groups. They are all metals with typical metal properties; for example they form ionic compounds with halogens and they conduct electricity and heat very well. When mixed with other metals, they make a variety of alloys. ❑

Name three transition metals and list their most important uses.

1 ....

2 ....

3 ....

C13 The transition metals join to non-metals to form ionic compounds. The metal ion can have a different valency depending on circumstances, for example copper(I) chloride ($CuCl$) and copper(II) chloride ($CuCl_2$). Transition metal compounds are sometimes coloured because the positive metal ion attracts other molecules called **ligands**. If the metal valency changes during a reaction then the colour may change too. ❑

Which transition metal ion can be responsible for

a) **a blue coloured compound?** ....

b) **a purple coloured compound?** ....

c) **a yellow coloured compound?** ....

C14 A **chemical reaction**

- involves energy changes
- involves formation of new substances
- is not easily reversed. ❑

Some reactions are very slow, for example ....

Some reactions are very quick, for example ....

C15 The **rate** of chemical reaction is increased by

- increasing the concentration of the reactants
- increasing the temperature
- increasing the surface area of the reactants (by breaking them into smaller pieces)
- adding a catalyst. ❑

The first diagram below shows a reaction in progress. Look at the other diagrams and write down whether the reaction rate will *increase* or *decrease*.

1M hydrochloric acid

calcium carbonate

....

C16 In a reaction, the reactant particles must **collide**. The rate of reaction depends on the number of **successful collisions**. ❏

Draw lines to match each factor with the correct description of how it changes the reaction rate.

increased temperature

decreased particle
size of reactants

catalyst present

increased concentration
of reactants

more particles so
more collisions

more energy to activate
more successful collisions

more particles touching
so more collisions

particles better positioned so
more successful collisions

C17 We use these ideas (from C16) about rates of reaction every day. For example, washing powders contain **enzymes** to dissolve biological stains. Enzymes are biological catalysts. ❏

Give an example from your own everyday experience of increasing a rate of reaction by:

using heat ....

breaking into smaller pieces ....

adding a catalyst ....

increasing the concentration of one of the reactants ....

C18 Enzymes are proteins. They act specifically on one kind of reaction and they are involved over and over again. Enzymes are denatured by heating above about 45 °C and by extremes of pH. In fact the optimum conditions for an enzyme catalysed reaction are often the same as those in its usual environment, often around pH 7 and a temperature of 35 °C. ❏

Label the graph to show where a) the highest rate of reaction and b) denaturation are most likely to occur.

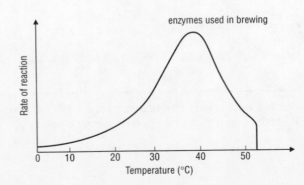

enzymes used in brewing

Rate of reaction

Temperature (°C)

C19 In industry it is common to find the rate of reaction being increased by

a) increasing the temperature (for example, in a blast furnace)
b) using a catalyst (for example, in the Haber process)
c) breaking into smaller pieces (for example, in cement manufacture)
d) using a highly concentrated reactant (for example, in an oxyacetylene torch). ❏

Read the notes below about the blast furnace (process (a) above) and then write similar notes for the other three processes.

a) Blast furnace: Iron ore reduced to Fe. Reaction with CO using heat.

b) ....

c) ....

d) ....

C20 Some chemical reactions are **exothermic** – they give out heat. Others are **endothermic** – they take in heat. ❏

Label the following reactions as *exothermic* or *endothermic*.

ice pack
liquids reacting

coal fire
combustion

acid
neutralisation

animal
respiration

....

C21 One important exothermic reaction is **combustion**. A fuel burns during combustion and releases energy and waste gases. Common fuels include coal, oil, kerosene, wood, petrol and candle wax.

petrol + oxygen → water + carbon dioxide (and heat energy)

wax + oxygen → water + carbon dioxide (and heat energy) ❏

According to the equations above, petrol and wax burn to produce .... energy and a waste gas

called .... Water is also produced.

A1 The **relative atomic mass** (A_r) of an atom of an element is its *average* mass. It is worked out by taking into account the abundance and mass of each of the element's isotopes. For example, natural chlorine is made of two isotopes. ❏

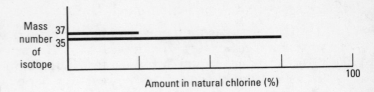

From the graph above, estimate the average mass of a chlorine atom? (*Hint:* **would it be nearer 35 or 37?**)

A2 The relative atomic mass of chlorine is calculated as follows:

$$A_r = \frac{(\text{mass of A} \times \text{\% of A}) + (\text{mass of B} \times \text{\% of B})}{100}$$

$$= \frac{(35 \times 75) + (37 \times 25)}{100}$$

$$= 35.5 \text{ amu (atomic mass units)}$$ ❏

Calculate the A_r of neon, which contains two isotopes: ^{20}Ne(90%) and ^{22}Ne(10%).

A3 The **formula mass** of a substance is calculated by adding up the relative atomic masses of all the atoms in the formula of the substance. For example,

$$H—F = 1 + 19 = 20 \text{ amu}$$ ❏

Examine the worked example and then complete the other examples:

Worked example:

calcium nitrate   hydrogen oxide   sodium fluoride   calcium carbonate

Formula: $Ca(NO_3)_2$

A_r: 40   14 × 2   (16 × 3) × 2

= 40 + 28 + 96

= 164 amu

A4 Different materials have different **inter**molecular forces (forces between molecules). The **intra**molecular bonds within a molecule also vary.

Label the *intermolecular forces* and *intramolecular bonds* in the diagrams below.

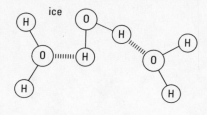

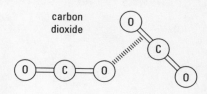

A5 A full outer shell of electrons is very stable. For example, Group 8 elements all have full outer shells; these gases are also very unreactive.

A6 Atoms can become stable by reacting to form compounds. In a reaction, the electrons are rearranged so that each atom has a full outer shell of electrons.

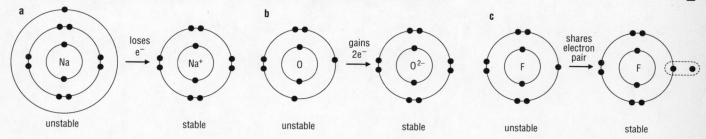

A7 Non-metals have a lot of electrons in the outer shell. In a covalent compound, the atoms share electrons to become stable, and a covalent bond is formed.

This diagram shows the outer shell electrons in a molecule of hydrogen fluoride. The H atom has a share of 2 electrons; the F atom has a share of 8 electrons. In this way, both atoms end up with a full outer shell. The shared pair of electrons is called a covalent bond. Note how the electrons are in pairs.

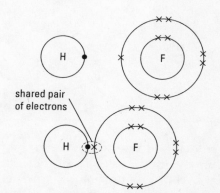

Draw diagrams similar to those in A6 and A7 to show how the atoms in a molecule of water (H_2O) and a molecule of ammonia (NH_3) have become stable.

A8 In covalent compounds, the valency number of each constituent is the same as the number of electrons that were originally unpaired. ❑

Draw the outer electron shell of the following atoms and write the valency number of the atom underneath. The first one has been done for you.

carbon   nitrogen   oxygen   fluorine

4

silicon   phosphorus   sulphur   chlorine

A9 Metal atoms have only a few electrons in the outer shell. In an ionic compound, electrons are transferred from the metal to the non-metal atom(s). The metal atom loses electrons and becomes a positively charged ion. The non-metal gains electrons and becomes a negatively charged ion. Ions of opposite charge attract and join to make a huge ionic lattice. ❑

Number the diagrams to show the correct sequence of events in the formation of the ionic lattice of sodium chloride.

A10 The valency number of each constituent of an ionic compound is the same as the charge on the ion. ❑

Complete the table below.

	Metal						Non-metal
Group	1	2	3	4	5	6	7
Electrons in outer shell	1				5		
To become stable		lose			gain		
	1				3		
Ion formed	+				3−		
Example	Na$^+$				N^{3-}		

A11 The number of electrons in the outer electron shell of an atom therefore indicates

- whether the atom is a metal or a non-metal
- whether it forms ionic or covalent compounds
- the group and valency (and thus chemical properties) of the element. ❑

A12 Elements and compounds have many different types of structures, ranging from single atoms, through **diatomic** molecules and **polyatomic** molecules to giant networks. Some examples are described below. ❑

Use the descriptions to sketch the structures in the spaces provided.

Copper Metallic lattice with positive metal ions attracted in all directions to a sea of negative electrons

Sodium chloride Ionic lattice with positive sodium ions attracted in all directions by six negative chloride ions

Glucose Covalent molecules held together by strong covalent bonds but with fairly weak hydrogen bonds between the molecules

Diamond Covalent 3D network of atoms tetrahedrally joined in four directions by strong covalent bonds

Graphite Covalent 2D network with atoms joined together in three directions to form plates. Weak bonds between the plates

Polyethene Polymer of small covalent molecules linked together in a chain by strong covalent bonds

A13 Covalent molecules are held together by strong covalent bonds. However, the attractions between the separate molecules are often weak. Many covalent substances therefore have low melting and boiling points, and are often gases or liquids at room temperature. They have no ions and so cannot conduct electricity. ❏

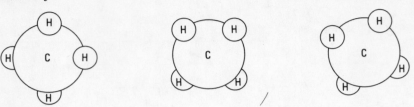

a covalent molecular structure

A14 A few covalent substances like quartz and diamond have high melting points. This suggests that they have giant **network** structures containing many bonds. The structure will break if enough force is exerted on it. This is why glass and ceramics are brittle. ❏

This diagram shows the structure of quartz (ground-down quartz is a major constituent of glass). Work out the repeating unit in the structure and then write down the formula for quartz.

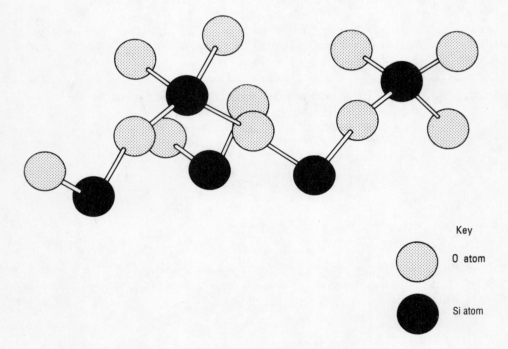

Key

O atom

Si atom

Formula:

A15 An ionic compound has a giant structure called an **ionic lattice**. In the lattice, the positive and negative ions are attracted to each other. The lattice is very strong, which is why ionic compounds have high melting and boiling points. However, it does break up when it is melted or dissolved in water. The charged ions are then free to move and electricity can be conducted. ❏

Label each drawing as fully as you can using one or more of the following words:

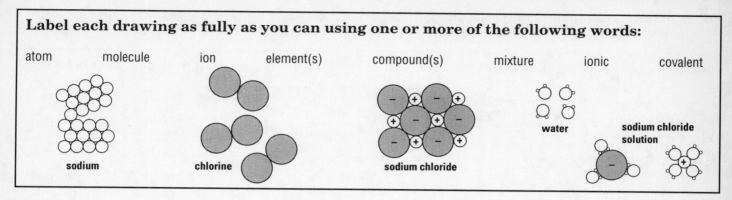

atom   molecule   ion   element(s)   compound(s)   mixture   ionic   covalent

sodium   chlorine   sodium chloride   water   sodium chloride solution

A16 An ionic solution conducts electricity. This passage of electricity through an ionic solution produces elements at the electrodes. This is called **electrolysis** (breaking up by using electricity). A covalent compound does not usually dissolve in water. If it does, it has no free ions and cannot conduct electricity. ❑

Identify the elements that are being produced in these two experiments.

Electrolysis of copper sulphate

....

....

Electrolysis of acidified water

....

....

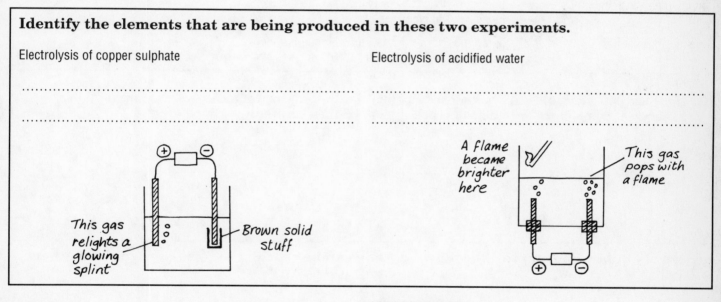

A17 Metals have a regular **crystalline** structure. The metallic lattice is **close-packed** – many atoms are present in a small space and the metal is therefore dense. The diagram on the right shows how the metallic structure enables the metal to be pulled into a wire. ❑

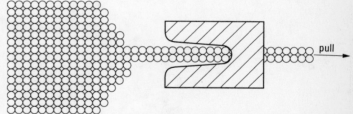

Draw a diagram similar to the one above to show the effect of alloying.

B1 Hydrocarbons are molecules containing hydrogen and carbon only. Two important families (homologous series) of hydrocarbons are **alkanes** and **alkenes**.

Some data are given below for the alkanes; write the corresponding data for the alkenes.

	Alkanes	Alkenes
first in series	methane	
molecular formula	CH_4	
structural formula	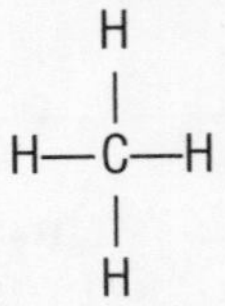	
general formula for the series	C_nH_{2n+2}	
trend in physical properties	boiling point and viscosity increase as molecules get bigger	
chemical properties	small ones burn well; decolorise bromine water slowly; single C—C bonds so fairly unreactive	

B2 Hydrocarbon molecules can be cracked (by heat in the presence of a catalyst) to form smaller molecules. Some of the products of cracking will be unsaturated.

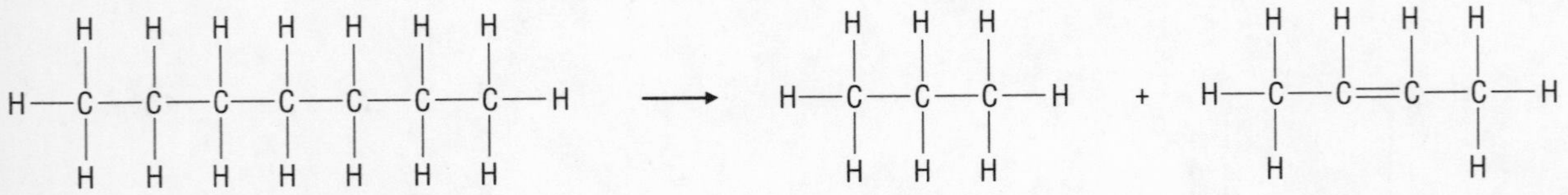

heptane C_7H_{16} → propane C_3H_8 + butene C_4H_8

Draw a similar diagram to show how heptane can be cracked to form pentane and ethene.

B3 Many modern materials contain **polymers**. A polymer is made by joining small **monomers** together.

Addition polymers

ethene
(from cracking)

polyethene

add across a double bond

Condensation polymers

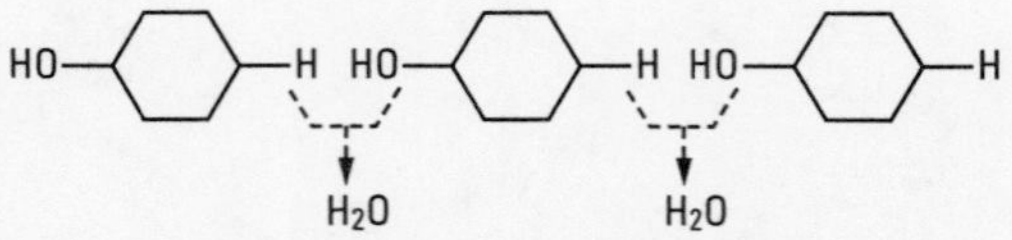

glucose

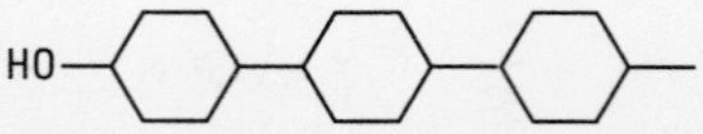

H_2O H_2O

starch

add by losing a small molecule

Underline the *addition* polymers in the list of polymers below. **Write a use for each one.**

polypropene   nylon   urea-formaldehyde   starch   polyvinylchloride   polyethene   protein

B4 Polymers have many useful properties:

- many are strong
- can be made into fibres
- easy to mould
- cheap to make.

It is now possible to design a polymer to do a particular job.

Complete this specification for a new polymer that is to be used as part of an engine housing in a new passenger aircraft.

Property	Specification
tensile strength	very high
thermal stability	
thermal conductivity	
melting point	above 1500 °C
boiling point	
solubility in water	
compression strength	
thermoplasticity	
biodegradability	

B5 Plastics and fibres are polymers. They have a thread-like structure, which is sometimes **cross-linked**. The amount of cross-linking affects the properties of the material.

Predict the properties of the materials below, and list them underneath each diagram.

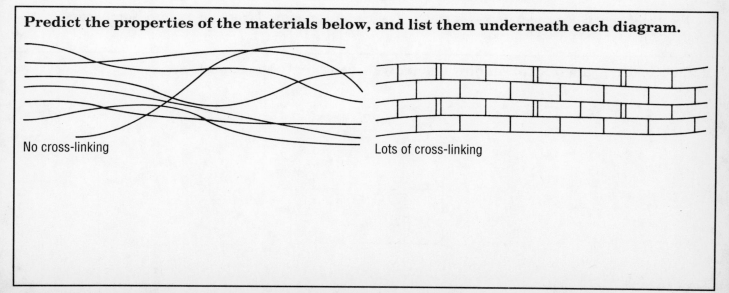

No cross-linking

Lots of cross-linking

B6 Metals are extracted from ores. The way in which any metal is extracted depends on its reactivity.❑

Complete the table to illustrate this point.

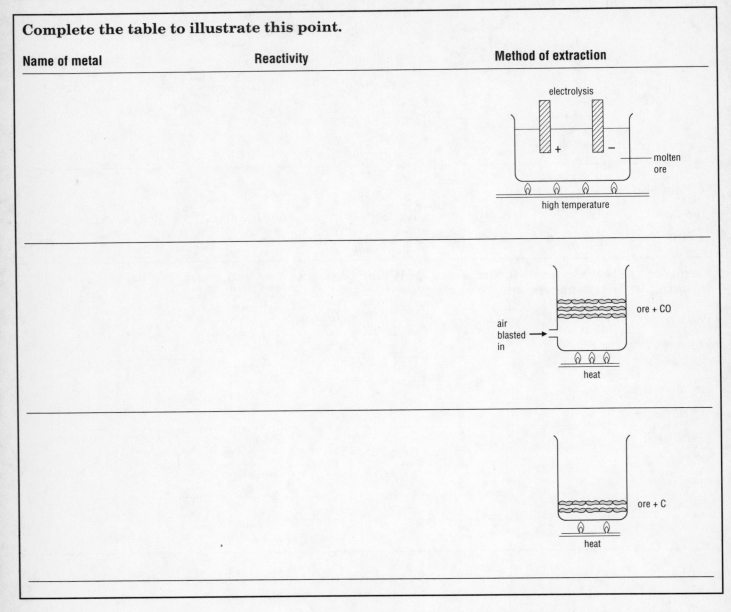

Name of metal	Reactivity	Method of extraction

B7 Electrolysis can be used to purify a metal. The metal is removed from the impure sample and deposited on the pure electrode. ❑

Label the diagram to explain how electrolysis can purify the sample.

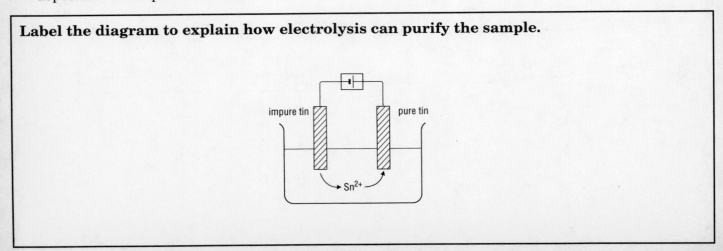

B8 Rusting and burning are **oxidation** reactions.

- Burning: fuel + oxygen → oxides (like carbon dioxide)
- Rusting: iron + oxygen → iron oxide (rust).

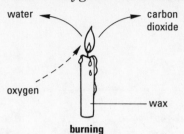

burning

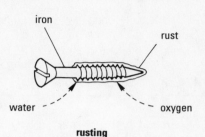

rusting

Rusting involves the corrosion of iron by reaction with .... and ....

B9 The rusting reaction needs water as well as oxygen. It can be slowed down by using electricity, coating with a more active metal or by **reducing** the amount of water and oxygen available to the metal. For example, the iron can be covered with paint or oil.

The burning reaction needs oxygen. It can be slowed down by reducing the amount of oxygen available.

Give three ways of slowing down the burning reaction.

1 .... 2 .... 3 ....

B10 Air also contains a lot of nitrogen. Nitrogen neither burns to form oxides nor forms compounds with other substances very easily. The gas is inactive because the diatomic molecule is bonded by three strong covalent bonds.

Draw a representation of the bonding in the nitrogen molecule.

B11 Nitrogen from the atmosphere is used to make fertilisers. First it is forced to join to hydrogen to make ammonia.

Complete the labelling of the diagram to show the essential features of the manufacture of ammonia from atmospheric nitrogen using the Haber process.

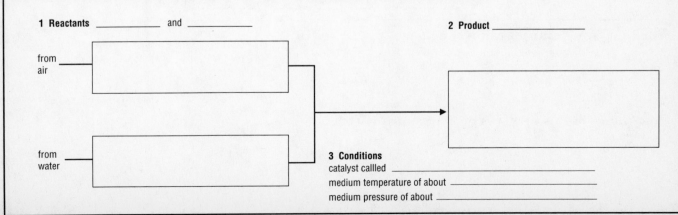

1 Reactants _____ and _____

2 Product _____

from air

from water

3 Conditions
catalyst callled _____
medium temperature of about _____
medium pressure of about _____

B12 Ammonia can be converted to soluble ammonium salts. These are then used as fertilisers. ❏

> **Complete these examples of fertilisers:**
>
> a) ammonium sulphate, made by reacting ammonia with sulphuric acid.
>
> b) ammonium nitrate, made by reacting ammonia with ....
>
> c) ammonium phosphate, made by ....

B13 Plants must absorb three main elements from the soil in order to grow well. These are nitrogen, phosphorus and potassium. Chemical fertilisers are described in terms of NPK values because they add these elements to the soil.

The fertilisers dissolve into rainwater, enter the soil and are taken up quickly by plant roots. The plants grow very quickly soon after, a great advantage to farmers and gardeners.

There are some possible disadvantages too because the fertilisers may be carried in solution into rivers and lakes, and into drinking water. ❏

> **Use all the following words to explain in sentences how too much fertiliser on fields could be dangerous.**
>
> dissolve   algae   green water   use up oxygen   organisms suffocate   eutrophication
>
> drinking water   may cause cancer   blue baby syndrome   blood cannot carry enough oxygen   decomposer microbes

B14 Single atomic particles are very small and impossible to weigh. We therefore use a quantity called the **mole** to measure the amount of a substance. The formula mass in grams of a substance contains 1 mole of particles, which is 6×10^{23} in number.

The number of moles, the mass and the formula mass are related. This triangle can be used to help you remember how: ❏

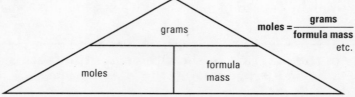

$$\text{moles} = \frac{\text{grams}}{\text{formula mass}}$$
etc.

> a) **Work out how many grams there are in 2 moles of $CaCO_3$.**
>
>
> b) **How many moles are there in 50 g of $CaCO_3$?**

B15 The idea of the mole can be used with equations to calculate the quantity of product produced per mole of reactant. In any calculation from an equation you must always use the following steps:

- word equation: carbon + oxygen → carbon monoxide
- balanced equation: $2C$ + O_2 → $2CO$
  (2 atoms) (1 molecule) (2 molecules)
- moles: 2 moles 1 mole 2 moles
- in grams: 2×12 32 g $2 \times (12 + 16)$
  = 24 g = 56 g

Note that:
- the moles do not balance on each side of the equation, but the grams do
- there is a line drawn across the page underneath the working. ❑

B16 The kind of working shown in B15 can be used to answer **calculation questions**. For example, how many grams of sodium oxide are produced by completely burning 2 moles of sodium?

word equation: sodium + oxygen → sodium oxide
balanced equation: $4Na$ + O_2 → $2Na_2O$
moles: 4 moles 1 mole 2 moles
in grams: 4×23 32 g $2 \times (46 + 16)$
  = 92 g = 124 g

If the figures for Na are halved to become 2 moles then those for Na_2O will also be halved to become 62 g. ❑

Use the calculation above to work out how many grams of oxygen are required to burn:

2 moles of Na   10 moles of Na
46 g of Na   9.2 g of Na

B17 Mass is conserved during a chemical reaction. The masses of the reacting substances when added together are the same as the masses of the product substances.

$$Mg \quad + \quad O_2 \quad \rightarrow \quad 2MgO$$
moles 1 mole 1 mole 2 moles
grams 24 g 32 g 66 g

$$24 + 32 = 66$$ ❑

B18 Formulae can be worked out by moving backwards through the steps outlined in B17. For example, you may burn 0.16 g of magnesium and find that it forms 0.27 g of magnesium oxide. So 0.16 g of magnesium has joined with 0.11 g of oxygen. You can work out the formula of the oxide as follows:

	Mg	**O**
Mass (g)	0.16 g	0.11 g
A_r	24	16
Moles = $\dfrac{g}{A_r}$	$\dfrac{0.16}{24}$	$\dfrac{0.11}{16}$
	= 0.0067	= 0.0068

Formula = $Mg_{67}O_{68}$

This is approximately Mg_1O_1 or MgO ❑

Complete this example.

	Cu	**O**
Mass (g)	0.87 g	0.11 g
A_r	64	16

B19 The **volume** occupied by 1 mole of a gas is the same for all gases at the same temperature and pressure. This fact can be used in equations where some of the substances are gaseous. For example:

methane	+	oxygen	→	carbon dioxide	+	water
CH_4	+	$2O_2$	→	CO_2	+	$2H_2O$
1 mole		2 moles		1 mole		2 moles

For gases: 1 unit volume   2 units volume   1 unit volume

This means that if there were 20 litres of methane, 40 litres of oxygen would be needed and 20 litres of carbon dioxide would be produced. ❑

Use the example given above to fill in the spaces:

If there were 15 cm³ of methane, ... cm³ of oxygen would be needed, and

.... cm³ of carbon dioxide would be produced.

B20 Calculate the mass of carbon dioxide produced when 50 g of calcium carbonate react with excess nitric acid. ❑

word equation: calcium carbonate + nitric acid → calcium nitrate + carbon dioxide + water

balanced equation:

moles:

in grams:

_____

If 50 g calcium carbonate react, ... g carbon dioxide are produced.

B21 In the example given in B20, assume 1 mole of a gas has a volume of 25 litres. How many litres of CO_2 would be produced? ❑

B22 During electrolysis, the positive metal ions gain electrons (are reduced). The negative ions lose electrons and are oxidised. The numbers that are gained or lost depend on the charges of the ions.

 • **O**xidation **I**s **L**oss of electrons: **OIL**   • **R**eduction **I**s **G**ain of electrons: **RIG**. ❑

Write R for reduction and O for oxidation next to these equations:

$Zn \rightarrow Zn^{2+} + 2e^-$ .... $4OH^- \rightarrow 2H_2O + O_2 + 4e^-$ .... $NO_3^- + 2H^+ + e^- \rightarrow NO_2 + H_2O$ ....

$Ag^+ + e^- \rightarrow Ag$ .... $Br_2 + 2e^- \rightarrow 2Br^-$ .... $2H^+ + 2e^- \rightarrow H_2$ ....

B23 Half-equations are used to describe what happens to particular ions within a reaction. For example, solid zinc displaces copper ions from solution:

$$\text{zinc} + \text{copper ions} \rightarrow \text{copper} + \text{zinc ions}$$

The more active zinc atoms pass electrons to the ions of the less active copper. The two half-equations are therefore:

$$Zn(s) \rightarrow Zn^{2+}(aq) + 2e^- \text{ (change in zinc atoms)}$$

$$\text{and } Cu^{2+}(aq) + 2e^- \rightarrow Cu(s) \text{ (change in copper ions)}$$

Similar ion-electron half-equations are used to describe electrolysis. ❏

When copper(II) chloride is electrolysed, copper forms at the negative electrode and chlorine forms at the positive electrode. Translate the two half-equations into words.

At the negative electrode: $Cu^{2+}(aq) + 2e^- \rightarrow Cu(s)$

At the positive electrode: $2Cl^-(aq) \rightarrow Cl_2(g) + 2e^-$

B24 A mole of electrons has a total charge of 96 500 C. (This is known as the **Faraday constant**.) ❏

B25 To produce 1 mole of an element from its ions during electrolysis, $\boldsymbol{n \times 96\,500\text{ C}}$ are needed, where n is the number of electrons involved in the oxidation or reduction reaction.

To produce copper: Cu^{2+} + $2e^-$ $\rightarrow$ Cu
  1 mole   2 moles   1 mole
2 moles of electrons has a charge of $2 \times 96\,500$ C.

To produce chlorine: $2Cl^-$ $\rightarrow$ Cl_2 + $2e^-$
  2 moles   1 mole   2 moles
Again, 2 moles of electrons has a charge of $2 \times 96\,500$ C. ❏

B26 The total charge passed during electrolysis is worked out by using the formula:

$$\boldsymbol{Q = I \times t}$$
❏

Write down what the symbols in the formula above represent and what unit each variable is measured in.

B27 When the total charge that passes during an electrolysis has been worked out, we can use the relationship $n\mathrm{F}$ for 1 mole (see B25 above) to calculate how many moles of substances are produced by this charge.

For example, in copper production:

$$n\mathrm{F} = 2 \times 96\,500 \text{ C},$$

which is 193 000 C for 1 mole.

If 1930 C are used during an electrolysis, then 1930 divided by 193 000 of a mole of Cu will be produced. ❏

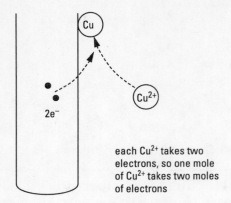

each Cu^{2+} takes two electrons, so one mole of Cu^{2+} takes two moles of electrons

B28 The air contains about 78.0% nitrogen, 21.0% oxygen, 0.9% argon, 0.03% carbon dioxide and small amounts of noble gases. ❏

Show the information given above on a bar graph or pie chart.

B29 The Earth is over 4 billion years old and for most of that time there has been no oxygen in the atmosphere. Present oxygen levels have been built up gradually over the last 2000 million years as a result of photosynthesis by green plants. The levels of gases in the atmosphere are kept fairly constant by balanced, natural processes. ❏

Name the gas which each pair of processes keeps in a steady state.

photosynthesis/respiration   fixing/decay   evaporation/condensation

....

B30 Convection currents inside the Earth cause the **plates** in the Earth's crust to move. Forces are exerted on the crust and this may cause layers of rock to break (causing **faults**) or bend (causing **folds**). ❏

Add these labels to the diagram below:

folding   faulting   anticline   force applied suddenly   force applied slowly

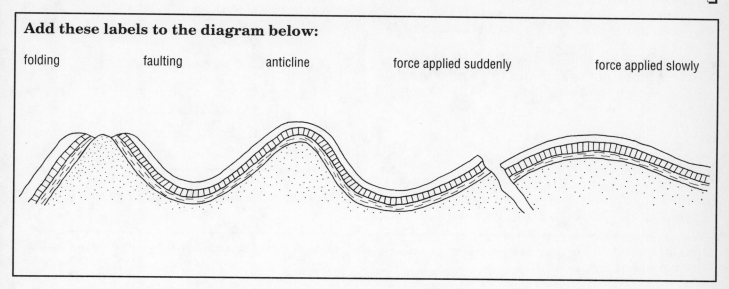

B31 The inside of the Earth is hot and much of it is molten. Energy escapes to the solid surface by **convection** currents, which cause magma to ooze out and release heat. This magma then solidifies and forms new crust. Elsewhere, old crust sinks into the mantle and is reabsorbed. ❏

Label these features on the diagram:

mid-ocean ridge   ocean plate   hot magma   direction of convection current

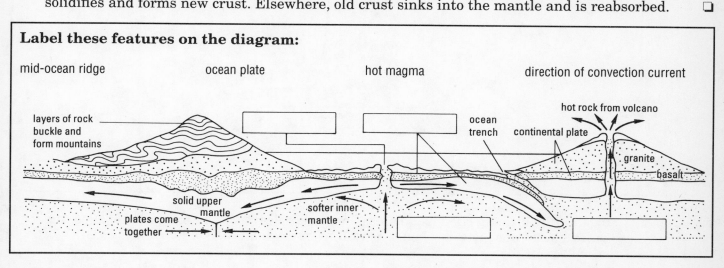

B32 The Earth's crust is divided into sections called **plates**. The plates move relative to each other because of the convection currents in the mantle. At the plate boundaries, several processes can lead to new features forming in the crust. **Plate tectonics** describe and explain this slow-acting yet dynamic change. ❏

Draw lines to match the processes with the features they create.

Process

plates slide past one another

plates collide and crumple at the edges

plates separate as new material is extruded

Feature

fold mountains and trenches

mid-ocean ridges

fault lines that are susceptible to earthquakes

B33 The Earth has a magnetic field. Although it is weak, it still causes magnetised iron to point to the North. It can also be used to work out how the rocks have changed over millions of years. ❏

C1 From the table on the right, it is evident that the number of electrons in the **outer shell** is the same as the group number in the Periodic Table. The outer shell is important for determining chemical properties because it is the first part of an atom to **collide** with another atom. This is why elements in the same group of the Periodic Table have similar chemical properties. ❏

Complete the table below.

Atom	Number of electrons	Arrangement of electrons
$_3$Li	3	2,1
$_{11}$Na	11	2,8,1
$_{19}$K	19	2,8,8,1
$_4$Be		
$_{12}$Mg		
$_{20}$Ca		

C2 A chemical reaction needs energy to get started. This is called the **activation energy** and it enables the particles to collide successfully. ❏

Mark the activation energy on the graph below (in the same way as the energy released in the reaction is marked).

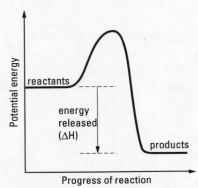

C3 Atoms join together by forming chemical bonds. Energy is released when bonds are formed and energy is required when bonds are broken. Such **bond energies** are usually measured in kilojoules per mole. ❏

C4 A chemical reaction involves bond-breaking and bond-making.

- If the bond-breaking energy is greater than the bond-making energy then the reaction is **endothermic**.
- If the bond-making energy is greater than the bond-breaking energy then the reaction is **exothermic**.

In the example below, methane is burned completely to produce water and carbon dioxide.

Reactants		**Products**	
$CH_4 + 2O_2$	$\longrightarrow$	$CO_2 + 2H_2O$	
break 4 C—H = 4 × 414	= 1656 kJ mol^{-1}	make 2 C=O = 2 × 724	= 1448 kJ mol^{-1}
break 2 O=O = 2 × 497	= 994 kJ mol^{-1}	make 4 O—H = 4 × 458	= 1832 kJ mol^{-1}
Total bond-breaking energy	= **2650** kJ mol^{-1}	Total bond-making energy	= **3280** kJ mol^{-1}

Overall energy = (energy in − energy out)
$= 2650 - 3280$
$= -630$ kJ mol^{-1} (The minus sign shows that the reaction is exothermic.) ❏

Complete an energy picture like the one in C4 above for the reaction $H_2 + Cl_2 \rightarrow 2HCl$. Bond energies in kJ mol^{-1} are: H—H (436), Cl—Cl (243), H—Cl (431).

C5 In a reversible reaction the activation energy 'hump' is low. Therefore the reaction can be forced forward or backward fairly easily.

Label the forward activation energy (E_f^A) and the backward activation energy (E_b^A) on the graph.

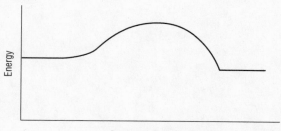

C6 The fertiliser industry uses raw materials to manufacture chemical compounds that contain nitrogen, phosphorus or potassium (for example, ammonium nitrate).

For example   **1** $N_2 + 3H_2 \rightleftharpoons 2NH_3$
then   **2** $NH_3 + HNO_3 \rightarrow NH_4NO_3$

Identify the reversible reaction above and give three ways in which the manufacturers ensure that a high yield of product is maintained.

Number .... is reversible.

High yield of product maintained by   1   ....

                                                  2   ....

                                                  3   ....

C7 Some manufacturing processes are based on reversible reactions. Examples are the Haber process and the Contact process. ❏

> **Which reaction is which? Label one reaction the Haber process and one reaction the Contact process.**
>
> $$2SO_2 \quad + \quad O_2 \quad \xrightleftharpoons[\substack{\text{1 atmosphere pressure} \\ 450\ °C}]{\text{vanadium(V) oxide}} \quad 2SO_3$$
>
> $$N_2 \quad + \quad 3H_2 \quad \xrightleftharpoons[\substack{\text{200 atmospheres pressure} \\ 450\ °C}]{\text{iron}} \quad 2NH_3$$

ATTAINMENT TARGET 4 (Sc4)
Physical processes

BIG IDEAS

A Electricity and magnetism can be controlled to serve human needs.
B Forces can speed up or slow down objects or change the shape of objects. Solids, liquids and gases react to pressure in different ways.
C Light waves, sound waves and water waves have similar properties.
D Theories and observations help to explain the Earth's place in the universe.
E Energy is transformed from one form to another when work is done. Power is the rate of transfer of energy.
F Radioactivity is all around us and can be useful as well as dangerous.

Sc4 FOUNDATION

A1 Electric circuits are conducting paths made up of a number of components. Circuits can be built by following a **circuit diagram** in which the components are shown as symbols. The flow of electrical charge round a circuit is called the **current**. ❏

Draw lines to match each component and its symbol to its correct function.

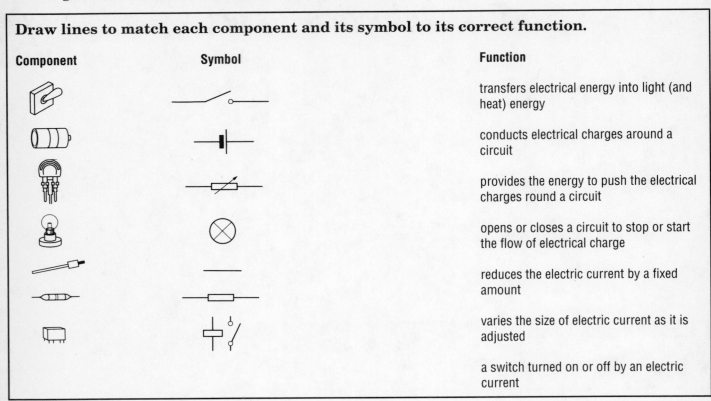

Component	Symbol	Function
		transfers electrical energy into light (and heat) energy
		conducts electrical charges around a circuit
		provides the energy to push the electrical charges round a circuit
		opens or closes a circuit to stop or start the flow of electrical charge
		reduces the electric current by a fixed amount
		varies the size of electric current as it is adjusted
		a switch turned on or off by an electric current

A2 Circuits can be set up with all the components in line – **series** – or side by side – **parallel**. ❏

Label each circuit's components as being in *series* or in *parallel*. Describe what happens in each circuit when the switch is open and when closed.

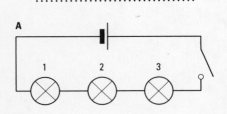

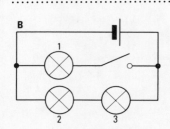

A3 In a series circuit, if one bulb fails the current stops. In a parallel circuit, if a bulb fails on one branch the current can flow through the other branch of the circuit. ❏

> **Look at the two circuits in A2 on page 94 again. With the switch closed, what happens to bulbs 2 and 3 in each circuit if bulb 1 fails?**
>
> In circuit A
>
>
> In circuit B

A4 Some materials conduct electricity better than others. They have a lower **electrical resistance**. Insulators are materials that do not conduct electricity very well. They have a very high resistance. ❏

> **Identify the resistance of each type of wire by ticking the correct column of the table or write each type of wire in the correct column of the table.**

Types of wire	Low resistance	High resistance
long wire		
short wire		
thin wire		
thick wire		
copper wire		
light bulb filament		

A5 When charge flows through a resistor there is a rise in temperature. This heating effect of an electric current is used in many domestic appliances. ❏

> **List four electrical appliances that depend on the heating effect of an electric current.**

A6 The energy needed to make electric charge or current flow in a circuit is measured in **volts**. The **voltage** in a simple circuit is supplied by the cell or battery. The more cells there are in a circuit the higher the voltage will be, and the higher the current. ❏

A7 The electrical energy of a circuit causes changes in the components in that circuit. For example, the electrical energy in a car headlamp circuit is transferred to the filament of the lamp. The filament heats up and glows to produce light. ❏

A8 Components such as bulbs offer resistance to the current. The more bulbs there are in a circuit the higher the resistance will be, and the lower the current. If the current through a bulb decreases the bulb glows less brightly. ❏

Complete the sentences to say what you could do to alter the current in the circuit shown.

Increase the current by adding .... or by

removing .... Decrease the current by

.... or by ....

A9 Current can be measured using an ammeter in units called **amperes** or **amps**. In a series circuit the current is the same at all points. In a parallel circuit the current splits at each branch. In all circuits the current is conserved – it is not used up. ❏

Ammeters are placed in series in a circuit. The positive terminal is always joined to the positive side of the circuit. Write the expected current readings in each ammeter in the circuits below.

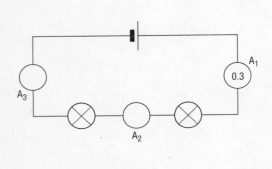
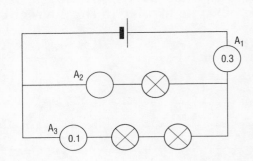

A10 A voltmeter is used to measure the **potential difference** (p.d.) between two points in a circuit. The voltmeter has a high resistance and is placed across (in parallel with) the circuit component. The positive terminal of the voltmeter is always connected to the positive side of the circuit. ❏

Draw two voltmeters in this circuit – one to measure the p.d. across the resistor and one to measure the p.d. across the bulb.

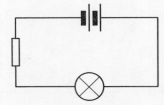

A11 Current varies with voltage in a range of devices. ❏

From the graphs, describe how current varies with voltage in the devices below.

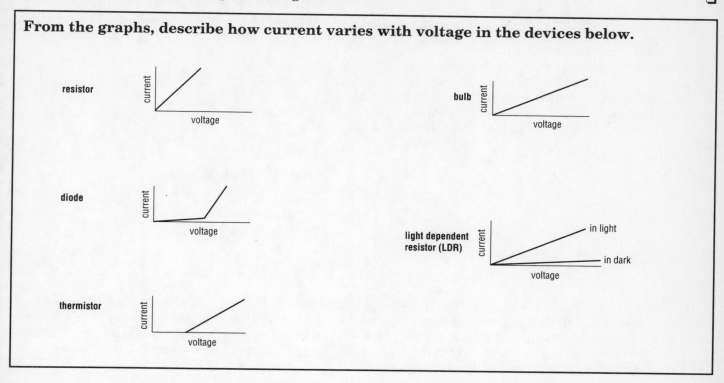

A12 Domestic electricity bills are calculated on the number of units of electricity used. One unit is 1 kilowatt hour. The immersion heater in a hot water tank has a power rating of 9 kilowatts. This means it uses 9 units of electricity per hour. A 100 watt electric light bulb uses 0.1 unit per hour. ❏

Electricity bills are calculated using this formula:
power of appliance × **time appliance is used** × **cost per unit** = **cost**
(in kilowatts)   **(in hours)**   **(in pence)**

Calculate the cost of using:
a) the 9 kW immersion heater for 2 hours at 8p per unit
b) two 100 watt light bulbs for 10 hours at 8p per unit.

A13 There are two types of electric current.

- Current that changes direction many times per second – called **alternating current** or **a.c.** Generators in power stations supply a.c. (which changes direction 50 times per second) as our mains electricity supply.
- Current that does not change direction – called **direct current** or **d.c.** Batteries produce d.c. Some power supplies convert mains a.c. to d.c.

❏

A14 Electrical **appliances** are made safe by

- having a correctly wired plug
- having a fuse in the plug to prevent too high a current flowing
- having an earth wire to conduct any charge that builds up to earth
- double insulating – making sure that no wires make contact with any metal part of the appliance that a person could touch. ❏

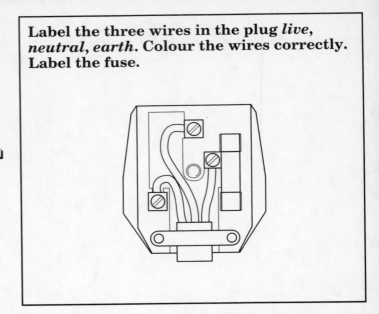

Label the three wires in the plug *live, neutral, earth*. **Colour the wires correctly. Label the fuse.**

A15 **Fuses** are always connected to the live wire, which supplies current to the appliance. The neutral wire returns current from the appliance. Fuses contain a wire that melts if the current is too high. This breaks the circuit and protects the appliance. **Circuit breakers** are much more sensitive to changes in current than fuses. If there is a sudden surge in current to the appliance a circuit breaker switches it off immediately. ❏

A16 There are three common fuses – 3 amp, 5 amp and 13 amp. The correct fuse to fit can be calculated using the formula:

$$\text{current} = \frac{\text{power rating of appliance in watts}}{\text{voltage (230 volts in the UK)}}$$ ❏

Calculate the correct fuse to fit in the plug of a:

table lamp with a 100 watt bulb

2000 watt electric fire

A17 When some materials are rubbed together, such as plastic being rubbed with a cloth, electrons are moved from one object to the other. The object that gains electrons becomes negatively charged. The object that loses electrons becomes positively charged. These charges are called **static electricity**. Like charges repel and unlike charges attract. ❏

Label the diagrams below using the terms *balanced charges* and *unbalanced charges*.

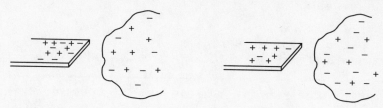

Draw arrows on each diagram to show the direction in which rod 1 moves.

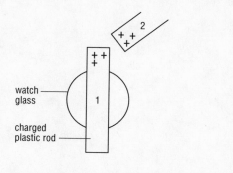

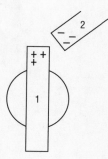

A18 When charges are unbalanced static electricity can jump (**discharge**) onto a conductor and cause a spark. This can be dangerous, for example if an object discharges near petrol or explosive gases.

□

Give two common examples of static electricity discharging.

1 .... 2 ....

A19 Electrostatic charges can be useful:

- rubbing a balloon charges it, and the balloon can be 'stuck' to the wall
- huge van de Graaff generators are used to accelerate particles in nuclear physics research
- photocopier.

□

A20 Magnets have a north and a south pole.

□

Write the word 'attract' or 'repel' under each diagram.

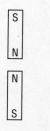

....

Write down a rule that describes how magnets behave.

....

A21 A **magnetic field** forms around any conductor carrying an electric current. This effect is used to produce **electromagnets**. An electromagnet is useful because it can be switched on and off. It can also be made stronger or weaker by:

- altering the number of coils of wire
- altering the size of the current in the wire
- adding or subtracting a soft iron core in the centre of the coil of wire.

Redraw the circuit and the electromagnet below with three alterations to make it stronger.

Your stronger electromagnet

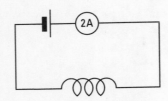

A22 Electromagnets are found in many everyday appliances such as telephones, loudspeakers, relays (magnetic switches) and electric motors.

Circle the electromagnet in each device.

Reed relay
The current in the control circuit passes through the coil of wire or solenoid. The metal reeds become magnetised and the current in the main circuit is switched on.

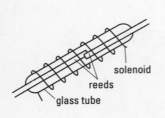

Loudspeaker
A paper cone attached to the coil of wire moves in and out as current passes through the wire. This makes the air vibrate creating sound.

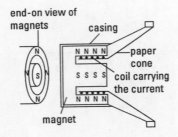

Electric motor
A soft iron core with a coil of wire around it is placed in the field of a permanent magnet. When the electromagnet is on its field reacts with that of the permanent magnet. The force produced makes the coil and iron core spin.

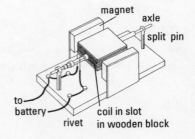

A23 When a closed coil of wire is moved between the poles of two magnets, an electric current flows in the wire. This is called **electromagnetic induction**. The same thing happens if the coil is held steady and the magnets are moved. If the coil is rotated in the magnetic field the induced current changes in size and direction. This is called **alternating** or **a.c. current**.

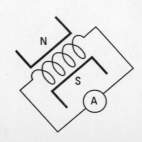

A24 The induced current can be increased by:

- using a coil with more turns
- using stronger magnets
- winding the coil on a soft iron core
- moving the coil faster. ❏

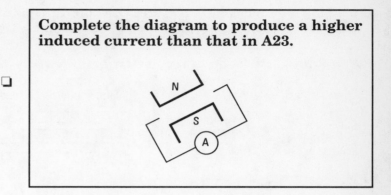

Complete the diagram to produce a higher induced current than that in A23.

A25 A simple bicycle **dynamo** has the same basic parts as an electric motor – a magnet and a coil. Usually the magnet rotates and the coil is fixed. ❏

Complete the boxes in each flow diagram using the list of statements.

current passed through coil   coil spins round   as wheel turns magnet spins round

rotating spindle raises load   induced current lights bulb

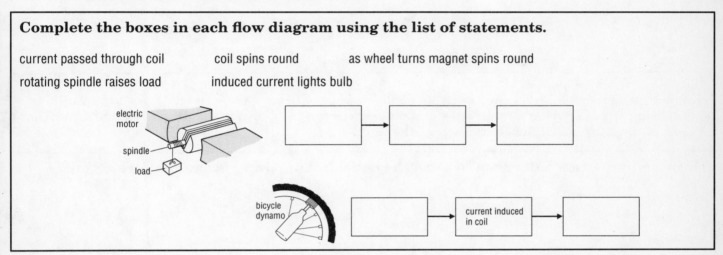

B1 **Force** is measured in **newtons** (N). ❏

B2 There are several different systems of forces:

- pushing or squashing   • bending   • pulling or stretching   • twisting   • tearing. ❏

What is the main force acting in each of these situations?

friction slowing a car	....	rolling a snowball	....
jumping on a sandcastle	....	magnet attracting a nail	....
charged comb attracting paper	....	ripping up paper	....
opening a jam jar	....	a ball falling from the sky	....

B3 An object can be affected by more than one force, and forces can act in different directions. A bridge is a good example. ❏

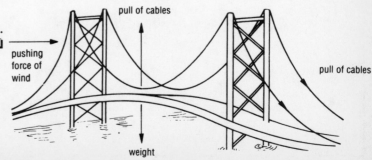

B4 Living organisms have features that allow them to withstand damaging forces. Manufactured objects are also designed to withstand damaging forces. ❏

Write down the type of force that each feature is designed to withstand.

hollow stems in waterweeds pillars supporting a roadway ropes to hold down a tent

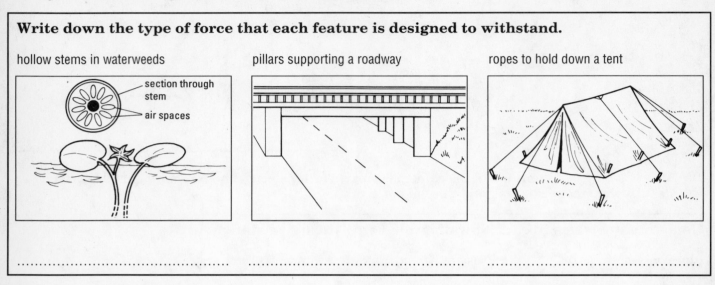

....

B5 When two objects interact they exert an equal and opposite force on each other. Sometimes the opposing force is obvious, sometimes it is not. Forces can be shown in diagrams using arrows. The size of the arrow can indicate the size of the force. ❏

Draw arrows on each diagram to show the equal but opposing forces that are acting.

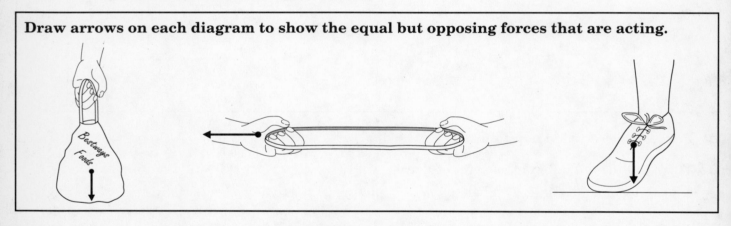

B6 When a force is applied to some materials such as a metal spring the material extends. The extension is proportional to the force applied. ❏

Show the effect on the spring of adding a second 1 kg mass.

Show the effect on the elastic band of pulling with three times as much force.

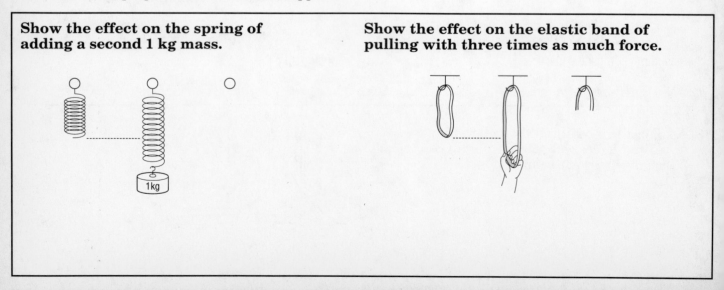

B7 When all the forces on an object are **balanced** the object will be:

- at rest
- floating
- moving at a steady speed. ❏

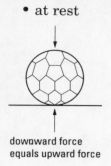

downward force
equals upward force

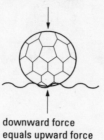

downward force
equals upward force

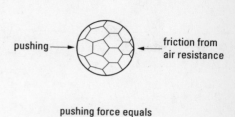

pushing → ← friction from
air resistance

pushing force equals
friction force

balanced forces acting on a ball

B8 When forces do not balance the **resultant force** will make the object:

- move more slowly (decelerate)
- move more quickly (accelerate)
- change direction.

For example, when a parachutist jumps from a plane.

❏

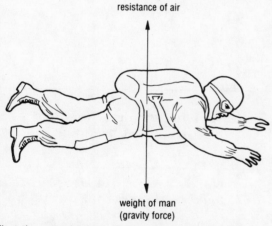

resistance of air

weight of man
(gravity force)

at first the parachutist accelerates because the force of
gravity is bigger than the frictional force of air resistance

friction force

gravity force

when the parachute opens the force of friction is bigger than
the force of gravity. The parachutist decelerates

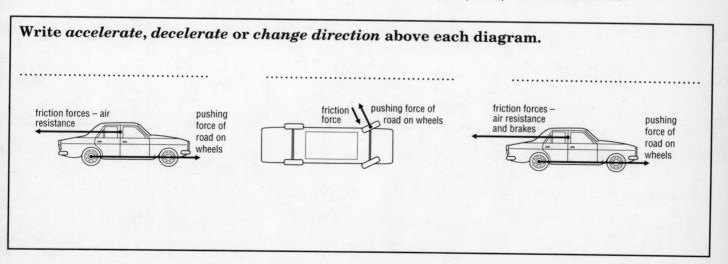

Write *accelerate, decelerate* or *change direction* above each diagram.

....

friction forces – air
resistance

pushing
force of
road on
wheels

friction
force

pushing force of
road on wheels

friction forces –
air resistance
and brakes

pushing
force of
road on
wheels

B9 The **average speed** of an object depends on the distance travelled and the time taken.

$$\text{average speed } (v) = \frac{\text{distance travelled } (s)}{\text{time taken } (t)} \text{ or } v = \frac{s}{t}$$ ❏

Write down the formulae for *time taken* and *distance travelled*. Calculate the answer to the problem.

time taken, $t =$

distance travelled, $s =$

What is the average speed of a car travelling 720 km in 9 hrs?

B10 The relationship between distance, time and speed can be shown in graphical form. In a distance–time graph the gradient of the slope gives the speed. In a speed–time graph the area under the graph represents the distance travelled. ❏

Use one colour to draw a line showing a faster speed. Use a second colour to show a slower speed. Label the lines.

Distance | Time

Write the words *accelerate*, *decelerate* and *constant speed* at the correct points on the graph.

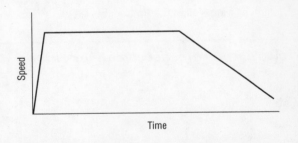

Speed | Time

B11 A vehicle's stopping distance depends on several factors. ❏

Place each factor in the correct column in the table.

Factors	Increases stopping distance	Decreases stopping distance
faster speed		
drier road		
deeper tyre tread		
smoother road surface		

B12 An object changes its velocity by changing either its speed or its direction. (Velocity has magnitude and direction. Speed only has magnitude.) **Acceleration is the change in velocity per second.**

$$\text{acceleration (m/s}^2) = \frac{\text{final velocity (m/s)} - \text{starting velocity (m/s)}}{\text{time taken (s)}} \quad \text{or} \quad a = \frac{v - u}{t}$$

For example, for a car going from 25 m/s to 39 m/s in 7 s,

$$\text{acceleration} = \frac{39 - 25}{7} = 2 \text{ m/s}^2$$

> **Calculate the average acceleration of a sprinter running a 100-metre race in 10 seconds. Her final velocity is 12 m/s.**

B13 When an object falls it accelerates owing to the force of **gravity**. Two different objects dropped at the same time will hit the ground at the same time because the acceleration of **free fall** is the same for both. (This assumes the objects have the same air resistance.) The force of gravity is normally rounded up to 10 N per kg.

> **Calculate the acceleration of each parachutist as they leave the plane. Use the formula force = mass × acceleration.**
>
> 60 kg parachutist   30 kg parachutist
>
>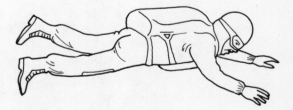

B14 The force of gravity also acts on an object thrown or fired horizontally. It will strike the ground at the same time as it would if it had been dropped vertically. ❑

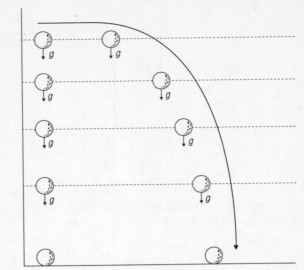

B15 A falling object does not continue to accelerate as long as it falls. When the force of friction caused by air resistance balances the force of gravity the object falls at a constant speed called its **terminal velocity**. A human falling from a plane has a terminal velocity of about 120 mph. ❑

B16 When a force presses on a small area, it exerts a large **pressure**. The same force applied to a larger area exerts less pressure. For example, the same person exerts a different amount of pressure on the ground depending on the shoes they wear. ❑

the force spread over a smaller area

the force spread over a large area

B17 Pressure is measured in newtons per metre^2 (N/m^2) or **pascals** (Pa) in liquids. ❑

$$1\,\text{N/m}^2 = 1\,\text{Pa}$$

Cross out the two incorrect formulae for calculating pressure. Calculate the pressure in the example given.

pressure = force × area

pressure = $\dfrac{\text{force}}{\text{area}}$

pressure = $\dfrac{\text{area}}{\text{force}}$

force 800 N

area 0.3 m^2

B18 Liquids cannot be **compressed**. When a force acts on the surface of a liquid the force is transmitted through the liquid evenly in all directions. **Hydraulic** systems such as car brakes depend on this idea. ❑

C1 Energy can be transferred by **waves**. There are two types of travelling wave: **transverse waves** and **longitudinal waves**.

Transverse waves can be drawn like this. Light energy is carried by a transverse wave.

Longitudinal waves can be drawn like this. Sound energy is carried by a longitudinal wave.

Sounds can be produced when an object vibrates. The **vibrations** cause tiny pressure changes in the air, which are **transmitted** (passed) through the air in a straight line. ❑

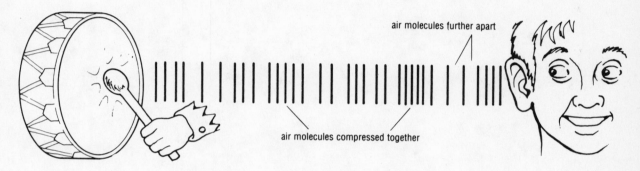

air molecules further apart

air molecules compressed together

C2 Water transmits both types of wave. Transverse waves can only move along the surface of the water. Longitudinal waves can travel through water. ❑

C3 All waves can be represented as a transverse wave diagram. A wave diagram has the three features shown. ❑

Longitudinal sound wave shown as a wave diagram

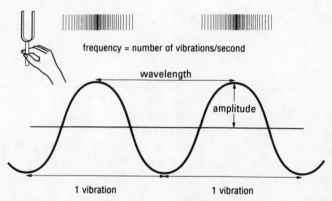

frequency = number of vibrations/second

wavelength

amplitude

1 vibration   1 vibration

Compared to the wave diagram shown above draw a wave diagram which has a:

greater frequency   longer wavelength   smaller amplitude

C4 Waves transfer energy without transferring matter. If a rope is attached at one end to the leg of a table and you flick the rope at the other end energy is transferred along the rope as a wave. ❑

Complete the second and third diagrams to show the wave transferring energy along the rope.

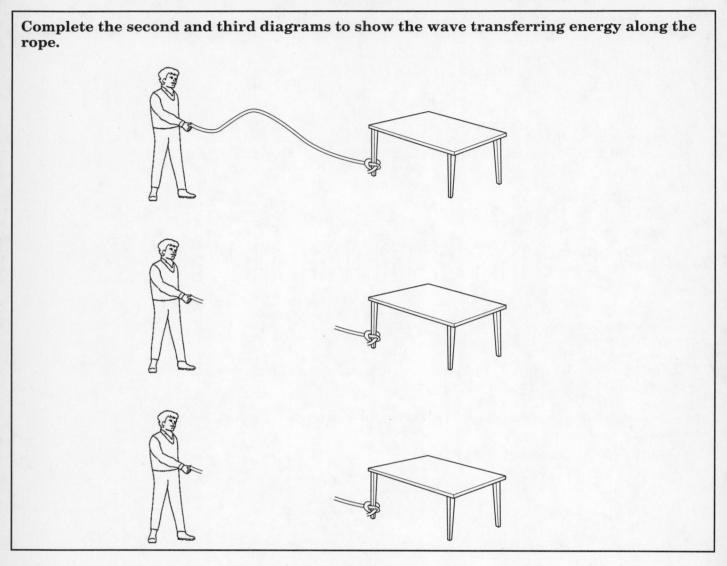

C5 Light, sound and water waves can be reflected and refracted. ❑

C6 When light, sound or water waves are reflected by a flat surface the **angle of reflection** is the same as the striking angle (called the **angle of incidence**). ❑

Draw arrows on each diagram to show the expected angle of reflection.

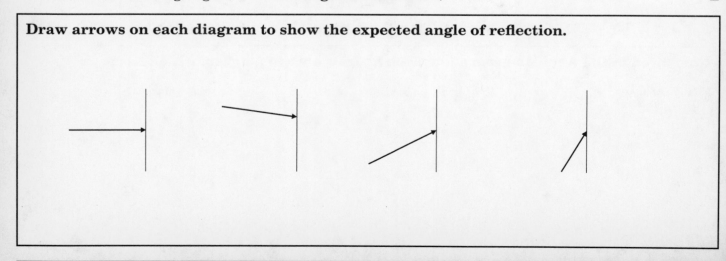

C7 When waves pass from one substance to another they change speed and wavelength but the frequency remains the same. Speed and wavelength decrease as the density of the material entered increases. If waves strike the new material at right angles they pass through in a straight line. If waves strike the new material at an angle they change direction slightly. This is called **refraction**.

Complete the diagrams to show refraction of light, sound and water waves.

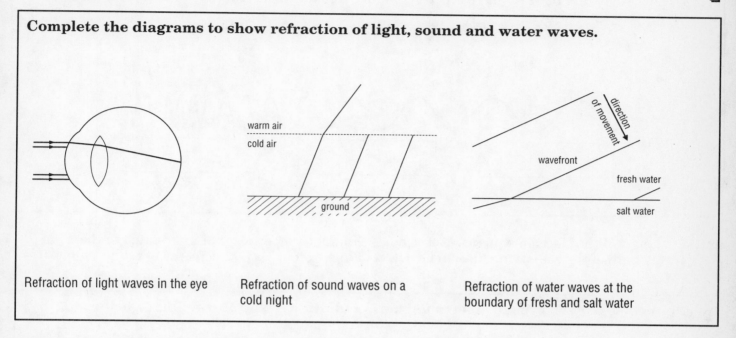

Refraction of light waves in the eye

Refraction of sound waves on a cold night

Refraction of water waves at the boundary of fresh and salt water

C8 When a ray of light passes from a dense substance into a less dense substance at an angle greater than the **critical angle** no light is refracted and **total internal reflection** takes place. This principle is used to transmit light along optical fibres, which are made of glass.

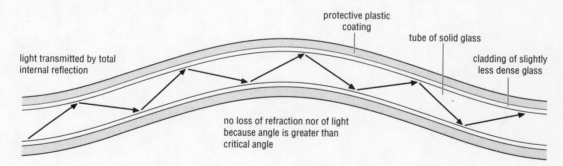

C9 Light consists of waves that carry electric and magnetic energy through space. Light is one type of **electromagnetic radiation**. Light has a range of wavelengths that our eyes can detect. Sunlight also carries ultraviolet and infra-red radiation, which we cannot see.

C10 Visible light is one part of the electromagnetic spectrum. This spectrum is made up of radiations of different wavelengths, from the shortest (gamma radiation) to the longest (TV and radio waves). All electromagnetic radiation travels through space at 300 000 kilometres per second. ❑

Label the positions of *gamma radiation*, *visible light* and *TV and radio waves*.

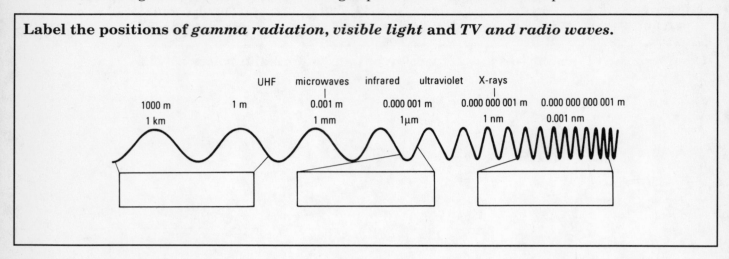

C11 Each part of the electromagnetic spectrum has different properties that are related to the wavelength of the radiation, and can be detected in different ways. Each type of radiation has its uses. ❑

Write the use of each type of electromagnetic radiation in the correct place below.

gamma rays   infra-red   microwaves   radio waves   ultraviolet   visible light   X-rays

Electromagnetic radiation	Wavelength	Properties	Detected by	Uses
radio waves	0.1–1 km	formed by electrons moving rapidly up and down aerial	tuned circuit or receiver	
microwaves	10^{-2} m	moving electrons produced by magnetron	tuned circuit	
infra-red	10^{-6} m	lamps, fires, sunlight	heating effect	
visible light	5×10^{-7} m	lamps, lasers, sunlight	visible, heating effect	
ultraviolet	10^{-7} m	lamps, sunlight	tanning effect on skin, fluorescence	
X-rays	10^{-10} m	X-ray tube, rays penetrate soft tissue, reflected by bone	photographic plate	
gamma rays	10^{-12} m	radioactive sources, highly penetrative	photographic plate	

C12 An **oscilloscope** can produce a graph of the changes in pressure caused by sound. Two important characteristics of sound can be compared using these graphs:

- loudness depends on the energy of the sound wave. The amount that the pressure of the air changes above or below the normal is called the **amplitude** of the change
- how high or low the sound is (the **pitch**) depends on the number of vibrations per second. This is measured in units called **hertz** (Hz). ❏

Label the pairs of oscilloscope graphs correctly. Choose from:

same pitch, different loudness   different pitch, different loudness   different pitch, same loudness

Describe the sound in each diagram by writing *high* or *low*, and *loud* or *soft* under each graph.

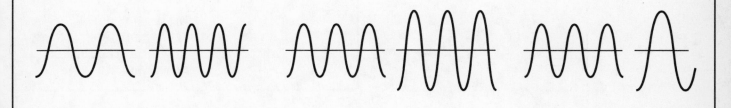

C13 In woodwind or brass musical instruments a column of air vibrates to create sound. In the stringed instruments the strings vibrate, whereas in percussion instruments it is the skin or metal that vibrates. Altering the length of the vibrating string or air column alters the pitch of the note produced. The shorter the length the higher the pitch. ❏

Put an *H* beside the instrument in each pair that would produce the higher note.

C14 Humans hear frequencies between 20 hertz and 20 000 hertz. Frequencies well above this (from 40 kHz) produce **ultrasound**. Ultrasound can travel through most materials causing no damage. Some sound is reflected back when it passes from one material to another. This effect has many uses:

- ultrasound scanners in medicine
- detecting flaws in materials
- sonar to detect depth of water, shoals of fish or underwater craft
- bats use ultrasound for navigation. ❏

D1 The **solar system** is the name we give to the Sun and the nine planets (one of which is the Earth) that **orbit** it. There are four inner planets and, much further away, five outer planets. For most of its orbit, Pluto is the outermost planet but at some points in its orbit it comes closer to the Sun than Neptune. All of the planets, except Pluto, orbit the Sun on approximately the same plane or level. ❏

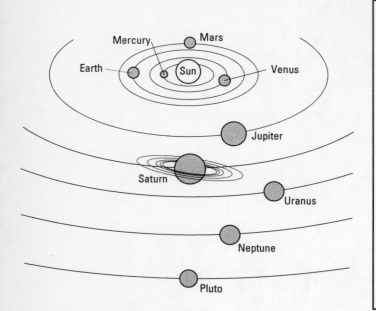

Write the names of the planets in the table below.

Planet	Time for 1 revolution of the Sun
	88 days
	224 days
	365 days
	687 days
	11.9 years
	29.5 years
	84 years
	165 years
	248 years

D2 The Earth spins or rotates from west to east as it orbits the Sun. It is tilted on its **axis** as it spins. This explains why we experience:

- differences in daylength at different points on Earth
- night and day
- the four seasons.   ❏

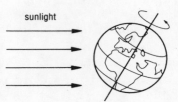

On the following diagram, shade in the night side of Earth. Label *night* and *day*.

On the diagram below, label *summer in northern hemisphere* and *winter in northern hemisphere*.

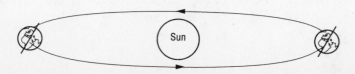

D3 The solar system forms part of a **galaxy** known as the **Milky Way**, which is part of a large system called the **universe**. There are millions of stars in our galaxy, which is in a local cluster of about 19 galaxies, and there are millions of galaxies in the universe. ❏

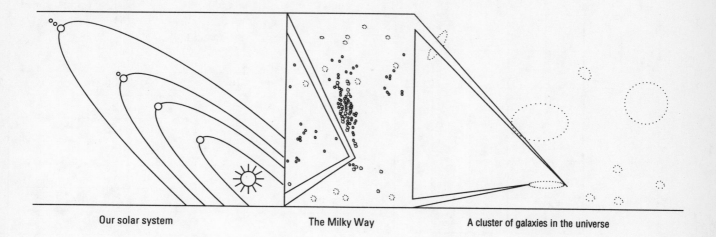

Our solar system   The Milky Way   A cluster of galaxies in the universe

---

Write the following in order of increasing size:

galaxy   planet   solar system   Sun   universe

....

smallest   largest

D4 Every object attracts every other object with a force, given by

$$\text{force} = \text{constant} \times \frac{\text{mass 1} \times \text{mass 2}}{(\text{distance between the masses})^2}$$

This is the force of gravity. ❏

Use the formula to complete the sentences with the words *increases* and *decreases*.

The force of gravity .... as the mass of the objects increases.

As the distance between the objects increases the force of gravity between them ....

D5 Gravity pulls all objects near the Earth towards its centre. This force on an object is called its **weight**. The Earth's gravity field at ground level pulls with a force of 9.8 N per kilogram – usually rounded up to 10 N/kg. ❏

D6 The gravity field of the Sun is so great that it has an influence throughout the solar system. For example, it:

- keeps the planets in orbit
- deflects the path of comets entering the solar system
- affects tides on Earth. ❏

D7 The Sun generates heat by **nuclear fusion** and influences the surface temperature of the planets. ❏

Plot a line graph of surface temperature against distance from Sun. Label each point with the name of the planet.

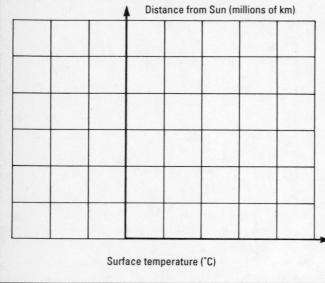

Planet	Distance from Sun (millions of km)	Surface temperature (°C)
Mercury	60	350
Venus	110	460
Earth	150	20
Mars	230	−23
Jupiter	780	−120
Saturn	1400	−180
Uranus	2900	−210
Neptune	4500	−220
Pluto	5900	−230

D8 Eight of the planets in the solar system fall into two groups with common features. Pluto is the odd planet out and may be a former moon of Neptune. ❏

Complete the following by writing the names of the planets in each group in the correct boxes:

Four inner planets

Four outer planets

- solid surfaces made of similar materials
- high density
- thin atmospheres

- fluid (gas or liquid) surfaces
- low density
- very dense atmospheres

D9 Distances in space are measured in **light years** – the distance light moving at 300 000 km/s would travel in one year. The nearest star to the Sun is 4.2 light years away. Such vast distances limit the amount of data that can be obtained from outer space by spacecraft. ❏

E1 We cannot detect **energy**. However, we can detect the changes that occur when energy is transferred from one material to another. For example, when

- a light goes on
- a clockwork toy starts
- a solar panel drives a motor. ❑

electrical to light   potential (stored) to kinetic (movement)   light to electrical

---

Complete the energy transfers in the two processes below. Choose the energy forms from this list:

heat   light   sound   nuclear   electrical   kinetic   potential   chemical

1 boiling water in a kettle: .... to ....

2 photosynthesis: .... to ....

Suggest an appliance or device in which each of the following energy transfers takes place.

3 electrical → sound: ....

4 kinetic → electrical: ....

E2 In many processes there are several **energy transfers**. For example, in a hydroelectric power station:

potential → kinetic → electrical ❑

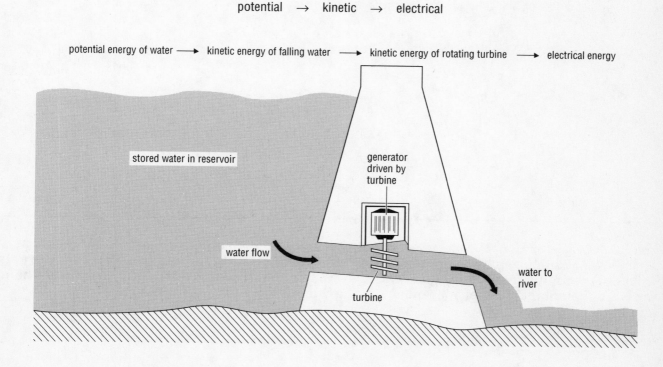

potential energy of water ⟶ kinetic energy of falling water ⟶ kinetic energy of rotating turbine ⟶ electrical energy

stored water in reservoir

generator driven by turbine

water flow

turbine

water to river

Write down the main energy transfers in a power station that uses fossil fuels.

coal, oil or gas burned   →   water turned to steam   →   steam turns turbine   →   electricity generated

.... → .... → ....

E3 No energy is lost in any energy transfer but some is wasted (changed to a form that is not useful). Because energy is **conserved** the total energy input always equals the total energy output. ❏

Underline or highlight the wasted energy below.

1 chemical reactions, e.g. combustion:

chemical → heat + light + sound

2 food chains:

chemical → chemical + heat + kinetic

Complete the following energy transfers, then underline or highlight the wasted energy.

3 playing a radio: electrical → .... + ...

4 battery-powered car: .... → .... + heat

---

E4 Electrical energy can be generated from **energy sources** that are either **non-renewable** or **renewable**. ❏

Write the correct heading – *renewable* or *non-renewable* – above each column in the table. Then write the correct energy sources from the list under each heading.

....

energy sources that will eventually run out   energy sources that are not used up

Energy sources list

coal	oil
wind	sunshine
gas	falling water
nuclear fuel	waves

E5 The Sun is the starting point for many of our energy sources. Energy transfer in a **food chain** depends on plants trapping solar energy in **photosynthesis**. Coal, oil and gas are all **fossil fuels** produced over millions of years from dead plants and animals. These were once part of food chains and were therefore ultimately dependent on the Sun. ❏

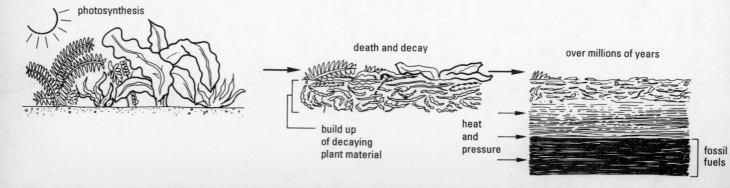

photosynthesis

death and decay

over millions of years

build up
of decaying
plant material

heat
and
pressure

fossil
fuels

Use the information below to draw a bar chart using the axes provided. Give the chart a suitable title.

If fossil fuels continue to be used at the present rate oil will last about 60 years, coal about 300 years and gas around 50 years.

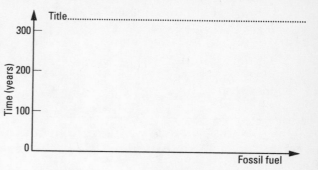

E6 Solar energy can be used directly as an energy source. It also transfers energy to wind and waves, which can be used as energy sources. ❏

E7 The unit of energy is the **joule** (J). 1000 joules = 1 kilojoule (kJ) ❏

E8 A hot object can transfer heat in three ways: **conduction**, **convection** and **radiation**.

- **Conduction** takes place in solids, liquids and gases. Metals conduct heat well by the flow of free electrons. The particles of a non-metallic, hot object vibrate rapidly and pass some of this energy on to neighbouring particles. In this way heat can be transferred through an object or to other cooler objects that it is in contact with. Some materials, such as metals, are good thermal conductors; others, such as glass, wood and air, are poor thermal conductors. Heat is conducted well through metal cooking pots.
- **Convection** takes place in liquids and gases. As a liquid/gas becomes hotter, it also becomes less dense. As this hotter liquid/gas is forced upwards through the cooler, denser liquid/gas, convection currents are set up. Water in an electric kettle is brought to the boil in this way.
- **Radiation** takes place through air or space. As particles vibrate they transfer some of their heat energy in the form of electromagnetic waves. These can pass through a vacuum, and this is how heat reaches us from the Sun through space. ❏

Summarise the information above in the following table.

	Radiation	Convection	Conduction
heat transfer through		liquids/gases	
heat transfer by			passing vibrations through neighbouring particles in non-metals or free electrons in metals
one example			

E9 Within a liquid the particles move at a range of velocities. Some move fast enough to overcome the forces of attraction between molecules at the surface of the liquid and they escape. This is called **evaporation**. The total energy of the liquid is reduced and so its temperature falls. This accounts for the cooling effect of evaporation. ❏

E10 Objects designed to reduce heat loss must prevent conduction, convection and radiation. For example, in a vacuum flask:

- the internal mirror surface reflects radiated heat back into the liquid
- the inner container is made of glass – a poor conductor

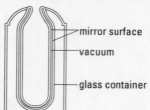

mirror surface

vacuum

glass container

- the system is closed, avoiding heat loss by convection
- the internal vacuum prevents heat loss by conduction or convection. ❏

Houses are designed to prevent heat loss. Which type of losses – convection, conduction or radiation – are avoided by the measures shown below?

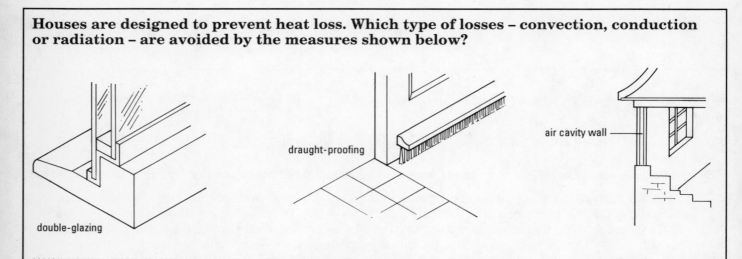

double-glazing

draught-proofing

air cavity wall

....

E11 Work has a particular meaning in science. Work is the transfer of energy by a force moving its point of application in the direction of the force. **Power** is a measure of the rate at which work is done or energy is transferred. These formulae are used to calculate work done and power:

- work done = force × distance moved in the direction of the force

- power = $\dfrac{\text{work done}}{\text{time}}$

For example, when a girl with a weight of 300 N runs to the top of 3 m high stairs in 12 s:

work done against gravity = 300 × 3 = 900 joules

power = 900/12 = 75 watts ❏

Calculate work done and power.

work done =   power =

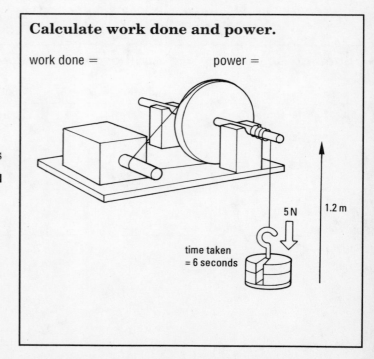

5 N

1.2 m

time taken = 6 seconds

E12 In electrical terms, power is a measure of the rate of energy transfer. It is calculated from:

$$\text{power (watts)} = \frac{\text{energy transferred (joules)}}{\text{time (seconds)}}$$

❏

E13 The power rating of an electrical appliance tells us how much energy it uses each second.

- 1 watt = 1 joule per second
- 1 kilowatt = 1000 joules per second

The power rating of a device depends on the supply voltage and the current through the device. The supply voltage in our homes is 230 volts.

$$\text{power (watts)} = \text{voltage (volts)} \times \text{current (amperes) or } P = VI$$

Rearrange the formula given in E13 to show the formulae for calculating current and voltage.

$I =$

What is the power rating of an electric kettle taking 9.6 amps at 230 volts?

$V =$

What is the power rating of a 3-bar electric fire taking 12.5 amps at 230 volts?

What current flows in a light bulb off a supply voltage of 230 volts with a power rating of 60 watts?

F1 Some atoms are **radioactive**. They have an unstable nucleus which finally becomes more stable by breaking up and emitting alpha particles, beta particles or gamma radiation. This is called **radioactive decay** and it is a random process. Alpha (α) and beta (β) radiation can be detected by using a Geiger-Müller tube to count the particles or by causing the particles to leave tracks in a cloud chamber.

Label the different types of radiation in the diagram _alpha_, _beta_ or _gamma_.

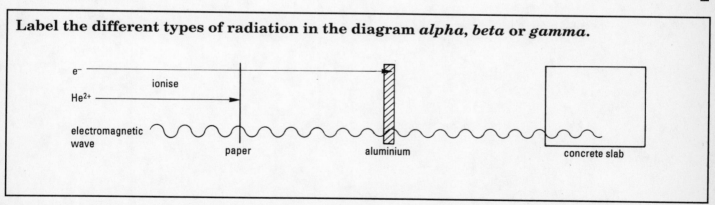

F2 Natural sources of radiation produce a low level of **background radiation**.

Add one example of sources of background radiation to the list below.

- fall-out from nuclear testing
- radiation from outer space
- radiation from isotopes in rock

F3 Radioisotopes are useful. The radiation from them can be used directly in various ways, for example to trace something that is difficult to see, to kill cancer cells, to measure very small distances, to show up hidden cracks in metal, to date ancient objects, etc. It can also be used indirectly to make electrical energy. ❏

Rearrange the steps by writing the letters in the correct boxes below to show how fission is used to generate electrical power.

a) A chain reaction begins and a lot of heat energy is released. This reaction is controlled.

b) The hot substance transfers heat to water in a steam generator.

c) A radioisotope (like U^{235}) is split by slow-moving neutrons. It releases energy and more neutrons.

d) The steam is used to move the turbine, which then makes electricity.

e) The heat energy is used to heat up water or another substance like carbon dioxide.

f) These neutrons split more nuclei and release even more energy and yet more neutrons.

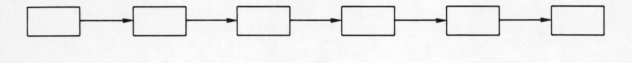

F4 Radioisotopes can also be dangerous. The **radiation** can cause harm to living things by breaking chemical bonds and by ionising molecules in the body. Such change can induce cancer or damage sex cells and cause mutations. This is why nuclear waste, which is radioactive and toxic, must be transported and stored with great care. ❏

A1 Electricity needs:

- an electric charge that is free to move – this is the current, measured in **amperes** (amps) using an **ammeter**
- energy to move the electric charge – this is the voltage, measured in **volts** using a **voltmeter**
- an electrical conductor that will have a low resistance, measured in **ohms**. ❑

A2 The electric charges that move in the wires of a circuit are **electrons** – part of the atoms of the metal conductor. Electrons have a negative charge. The charges that flow in liquids during electrolysis are free **ions**. ❑

A3 The relationship that connects current, voltage and resistance in metals and carbon (but not in any other materials) is

$$\text{voltage } (V) = \text{current } (I) \times \text{resistance } (R) \quad \text{or} \quad V = IR$$ ❑

In any circuit the voltage and current may change but the resistance is constant. The rule $R = \text{constant}$ is Ohm's law.

Write down the formulae for current and resistance in a circuit. Calculate the current flowing in the series circuit shown.

current, $I =$

resistance, $R =$

current flowing:

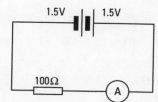

A4 Total resistance is calculated differently in series and parallel circuits.

In this series circuit:
total resistance $R = R_1 + R_2 + R_3$

In this parallel circuit:
total resistance $1/R = 1/R_1 + 1/R_2 + 1/R_3$ ❑

Calculate the total resistance in each of the circuits above.

series circuit:

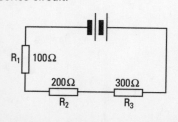

parallel circuit:

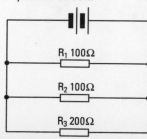

A5 The **power rating** of an electrical appliance is given in watts or kilowatts. This shows how much energy is transferred per second.

- 1 watt = 1 joule per second
- 1 kilowatt = 1 kilojoule per second

The power rating of an appliance is found using:

$$\text{power} = \text{voltage} \times \text{current} \quad \text{or} \quad P = VI$$

$$\text{substituting } V = IR \text{ gives } P = I^2R$$

$$\text{substituting } I = \frac{V}{R} \text{ gives } P = \frac{V^2}{R} \qquad \Box$$

Complete this table.

Appliance	Power rating	Voltage	Current	Resistance
car headlamp		12 volts	3 amperes	
electric drill	240 watts	240 volts		

A6 The total **electric charge** moved in a circuit is measured in **coulombs**.

charge moved (Q, in coulombs) = current (I, in amperes) $\times$ time (t, in seconds)   or $Q = It$ $\Box$

Rearrange the formula above to show how to calculate current and time.

$I =$ $t =$

A7 Voltage is a measure of the available energy per unit charge. When or if 1 coulomb of charge transfers 1 joule of energy as it goes through a component, then the voltage across the component (the potential difference, or p.d.) is 1 joule per coulomb. This is called 1 volt.

   $\Box$

Calculate the total charge flowing in a circuit carrying 4 amperes through a car headlamp for 1.5 hours.

A8 A **transformer** is made of two C-shaped soft iron cores each with a coil of wire wound round it. When a current is switched on in circuit 1 an electric current is momentarily induced in circuit 2. If the current in circuit 1 is steadily changed, a steady direct current is induced in circuit 2. If the current in circuit 1 is switched on and off, an alternating (a.c.) current is produced in circuit 2. ❏

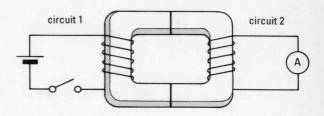

Label each circuit correctly using the terms *direct current produced* **and** *alternating current produced.* **Make a key for these components:** *ammeter, transformer, variable resistor, cell.*

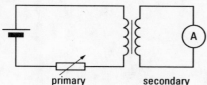

primary   secondary

....

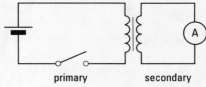

primary   secondary

....

Key:

A9 Transformers can be used to alter the supply voltage by **stepping** it up or stepping it down. The voltage in the secondary circuit depends on the ratio of the number of coils in the primary to the number of coils in the secondary.

Because transformers are nearly 100% efficient:

electrical power of the primary circuit = electrical power delivered by the secondary circuit (supply)

$$V_{primary} \times I_{primary} = V_{secondary} \times I_{secondary}$$ ❏

Calculate the missing values in diagrams b) and c). Complete the final sentence.

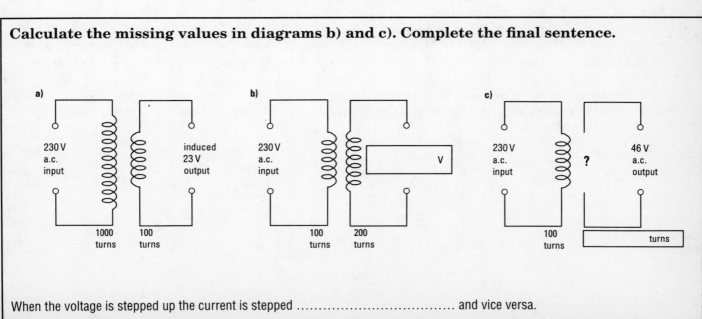

When the voltage is stepped up the current is stepped .... and vice versa.

A10 Electromagnetic induction is very important in the electricity industry for:

- producing electricity with **a.c. generators**
- stepping up the voltage using transformers before transmission. ❏

A11 In **a.c. generators** a central electromagnet rotates between fixed coils of wire where an alternating current is induced.

The shaft of the electromagnet is attached to a steam turbine. The turbine shaft rotates when steam is forced through the turbine blades. The steam is produced from water heated by burning fossil fuels in a furnace or by the heat from a nuclear reactor. ❏

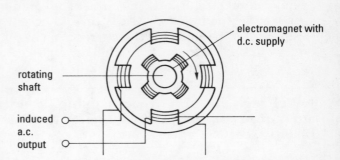

Complete the flow diagram using the words below.

a.c. induced   a.c. generator   turbine shaft rotates   turbine   produce steam

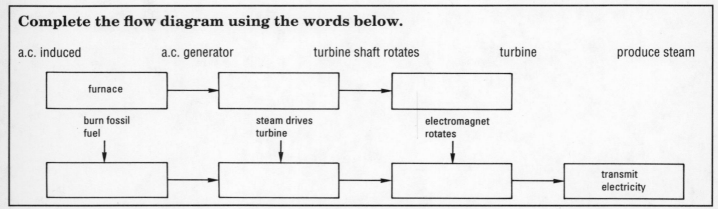

A12 Power stations produce electricity at very high voltage and high current. If it were transmitted like this, a great deal of energy would be wasted as heat in the electricity cables. The heat loss can be calculated from the formula $P = I^2 R$. Any reduction in current will reduce energy loss. A step up transformer allows electricity to be transmitted through the supergrid at 400 000 volts and very low current. Transformers in local substations step down the voltage to 230 volts for domestic use. ❏

B1 Velocity and speed are two measures of how fast a body moves. **Speed** has a magnitude only. It is the distance travelled divided by the time taken. **Velocity** has a magnitude and direction. It is the distance travelled in a particular direction in the time taken. A body can only move at constant velocity if it travels in a straight line. ❏

B2 Values for **acceleration** and **distance** travelled can be calculated from a **velocity–time graph**. The gradient of the line gives the acceleration and the area under the graph gives the distance travelled. ❏

Calculate the acceleration between points B and C on the graph and the total distance travelled up to point C.

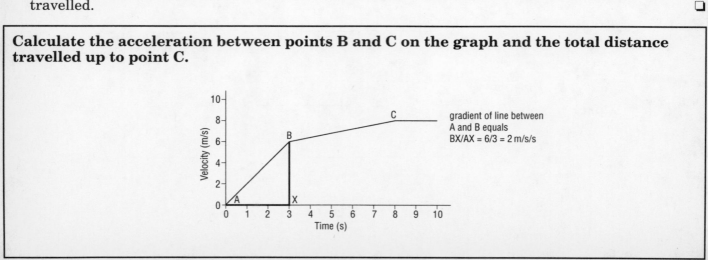

B3 To change the velocity of an object an unbalanced force must act on it.

$$a = \frac{F}{m} \quad \text{or rearranged} \quad F = ma$$

where F = force (N), m = mass (kg) and a = acceleration (m/s^2).

For example, a small force is needed to start an empty supermarket trolley moving. A larger force is needed to give a full trolley the same acceleration. ❏

B4 Car seat belts are designed to reduce the deceleration on the body by yielding a little when a car stops, and so reducing the stopping force on the body.

force (F) = mass (m) × acceleration (a)

substituting $a = \dfrac{v - u}{t}$

stopping force $(F) = \dfrac{m(v - u)}{t}$

Any increase in time reduces the stopping force and helps to prevent injury. ❏

B5 Car design also includes crumple zones around the front and rear bumpers. On collision these reduce the stopping time fractionally and so decrease the stopping forces. ❏

Calculate the stopping force for a 1000 kg car without crumple zones crashing to a stop from 10 m/s in 0.1 s.

Calculate the stopping force for a 1000 kg car with crumple zones crashing to a stop from 10 m/s in 0.15 s.

B6 A liquid can transmit an external pressure applied to all parts of the liquid. If a narrow cylinder is connected to a wider cylinder, both containing liquid, a small force applied at the narrow end results in a larger force at the wider end. This idea is used in **hydraulic** lifts and presses as well as in car brakes. ❏

Calculate the force exerted at B in the second diagram.

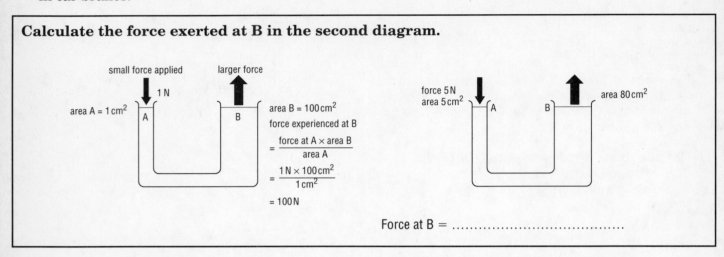

force experienced at B

$$= \frac{\text{force at A} \times \text{area B}}{\text{area A}}$$

$$= \frac{1\,N \times 100\,cm^2}{1\,cm^2}$$

$$= 100\,N$$

Force at B = ...

B7 The particles of a body move faster as the temperature increases. Internal kinetic energy of the particles is increased. In the diagrams below, the gas particles are in a box with movable sides. When it becomes hotter (increased temperature), they move about faster and collide more forcefully with the walls of the box (increased pressure). The walls are pushed out so that the gas particles take up more space (increased volume). The relationship between these three variables (for an ideal/perfect gas) is shown by the **gas equation**:

$$\frac{\text{pressure} \quad \times \quad \text{volume}}{\text{temperature}} = \text{constant value}$$

The mass of gas in each box is the same. ❏

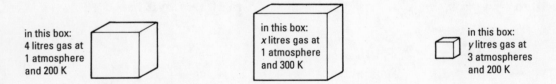

in this box:
4 litres gas at
1 atmosphere
and 200 K

in this box:
x litres gas at
1 atmosphere
and 300 K

in this box:
y litres gas at
3 atmospheres
and 200 K

To calculate x: **Now you calculate y:**

$$\frac{P_1 \, V_1}{T_1} = \frac{P_2 \, V_2}{T_2}$$

$$\frac{1 \times 4}{200} = \frac{1 \times x}{300}$$

$$x = \frac{300 \times 4}{200}$$

$$= 6 \text{ litres}$$

C1 A spring can be used to demonstrate the difference between a **transverse** and a **longitudinal** wave. ❏

Label the wave forms *longitudinal* **and** *transverse*. **On the longitudinal wave label** *areas of compression* **and** *areas of expansion* (rarefaction):

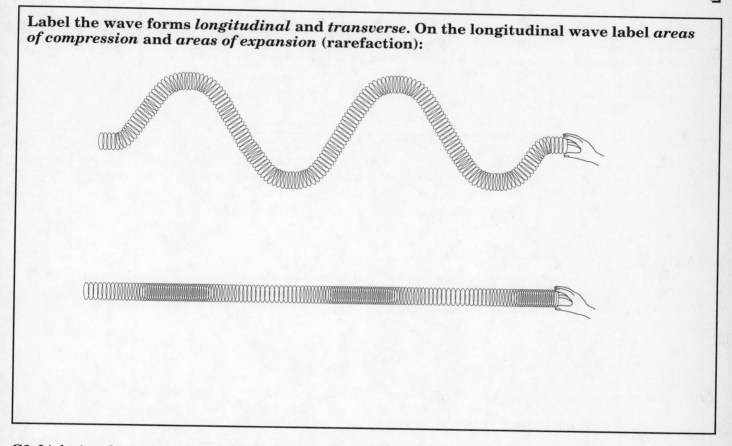

C2 Light is a form of electromagnetic radiation that can pass through space. These transverse waves do not require a medium containing particles for their transmission. Sound waves are longitudinal and are transmitted by the vibration of particles. They cannot pass through the vacuum of space. ❏

C3 Both light and sound travel through the air as **waves**. However, their speeds are very different:
- light travels at 300 million metres per second (3×10^8 m/s)
- sound travels at 340 metres per second (340 m/s). ❏

Explain *one* **of the following:**
a) **why you can see a ball leaving a cricket bat before you hear the thump,** *or*
b) **why you see the flash of a gun before you hear the bang.**

C4 The speed of a wave is related to its frequency and wavelength:

speed (velocity) (m/s) = frequency (Hz) × wavelength (m)   or $v = f\lambda$

This is true for all waves. ❏

Write down the *formula for wavelength* and the *formula for frequency*.

....

C5 When a wave passes through a small gap in a barrier it spreads out. This is called **diffraction** and applies to sound waves and water waves as well as all types of electromagnetic radiation. ❏

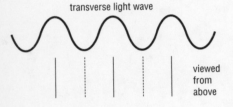

transverse light wave

viewed from above

diffraction through a gap

C6 Interference effects occur when waves meet. When two troughs or two crests meet in phase (together) they combine to form larger troughs or crests. If a trough and crest of equal intensity, moving in the same direction meet, they cancel each other. ❏

Draw the results of the two types of interference shown below.

constructive interference – waves in phase

destructive interference – waves out of phase

C7 TV and some radio signals are transmitted at ultra-high frequencies (UHF) and short wavelengths because these waves travel in straight lines and give a better quality of picture and sound than medium- or long-wave transmissions. A disadvantage is that they do not follow the curvature of the Earth and so are only suitable for transmission over short distances.

Transmitters and receivers must be positioned carefully for good communication. There have to be many transmitters, each operating over a slightly different frequency band to avoid interference. ❏

C8 The Earth is layered.

Draw the Earth's layers on the cut-away diagram and add the following labels:

inner core (solid)   outer core (liquid)   crust   mantle

ocean

land

C9 **Earthquakes** produce shock waves, which are recorded and analysed at **seismic** stations. These waves are refracted by different materials. This property has allowed scientists to establish that the core is metallic, probably largely iron and nickel, whereas the mantle is made of many compounds. The oceanic crust is mainly basalt and the upper continental crust contains a lot of granite.

D1 The force that keeps an object moving in a circle is called the **centripetal force**. This can be calculated from:

$$\text{force} = \frac{mv^2}{r}$$

where r is the radius of the circle.

This formula shows that doubling the speed increases the force required to keep the object travelling in a circle by a factor of 4.

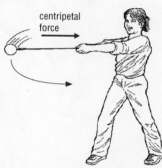

centripetal force

D2 Artificial satellites move in a circle round the Earth. The centripetal force that keeps them in orbit is gravity. There are low-orbit and **geostationary** satellites. Low-orbit satellites are on high-velocity orbits and are out of contact with their Earth tracking stations for some of the time. They are used for spying, surveying and studying the weather. Communications satellites and some weather stations are on geostationary orbits. These satellites are in high orbits travelling at a speed that keeps them over the same place on the Earth's surface.

The forces on low-orbit satellites are much greater than those on geostationary satellites because their speed is much greater and their orbit height is less.

Label the two geostationary satellites and the low-orbit satellite below.

D3 Many scientists believe in the **big bang theory** to explain the origin of the universe. This theory suggests that the universe began with an explosion about 15 billion years ago, which threw matter out in all directions. ❏

D4 Evidence for the big bang theory comes from:
- observations of the positions of stars, which suggest they are moving away from each other
- examining the quality of light from distant stars and galaxies. The **spectra** have longer wavelengths than expected. This **'red shift'** indicates that these bodies are moving away from Earth. ❏

D5 Scientists suggest that one of three things will happen to the universe:
- the universe will keep on expanding for ever
- the universe will stop expanding and reach a steady state
- the universe will stop expanding and then contract in on itself. ❏

D6 Stars are thought to follow a 'life cycle':
1. clouds of hydrogen gas are drawn together by gravity
2. nuclear fusion occurs when hydrogen atoms collide and combine to form helium and release light energy
3. eventually all the hydrogen is used up and the star becomes a **red giant**
4. depending on its size, the red giant can explode in a **nova** and form a **white dwarf**, explode in a **supernova** and become a **pulsar**, or collapse in on itself to become a **black hole**. ❏

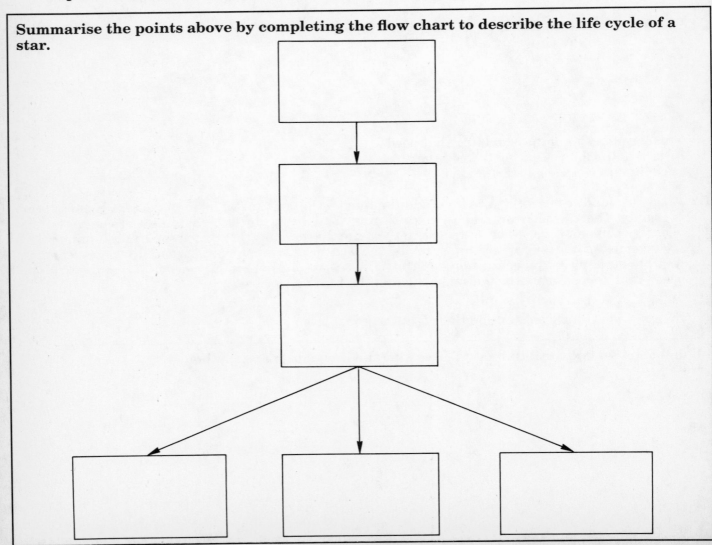

Summarise the points above by completing the flow chart to describe the life cycle of a star.

E1 We are often faced with a number of different energy options and choosing the best one can be difficult. The choice of energy source depends on balancing

- availability
- need for conservation
- financial cost
- environmental impact
- social cost.

Give:

a) one social cost of not using coal

b) one environmental effect of mining

c) one reason for conserving fossil fuels

E2 There is a move towards the use of renewable energy sources such as

- tidal energy
- wave energy
- solar energy
- wind
- biomass.

Biomass is organic material – plants, animals and their wastes. Biomass can either be digested by bacteria to produce methane gas for burning or converted to pellets that can be burned.

Write the headings *advantages* and *disadvantages* in the correct place in the table.

Renewable energy sources	
plentiful supply	supply seldom continuous
non-polluting	technology for collection still being developed
free	expensive to collect

E3 Energy **efficiency** depends on the amount of useful energy that comes out of a system compared with the amount put in. Some energy is always wasted in the **transducer** (the energy changer), often as heat produced by friction and as sound.

$$\% \text{ energy efficiency} = \frac{\text{useful energy output}}{\text{energy input}} \times 100$$

Calculate the efficiency in these two systems.

Energy input	Transducer	Useful energy output	Efficiency
chemical 2800 J	human muscle	kinetic 1120 J	
electrical 1500 kJ	electric fire	heat 1425 kJ	

E4 In any process, 'waste' energy spreads out into the surroundings. It is distributed amongst many particles and cannot be collected easily and put to use. For example, the internal combustion engine is only about 15% efficient. 85% of the energy released when petrol interacts with oxygen is lost to the surroundings. ❏

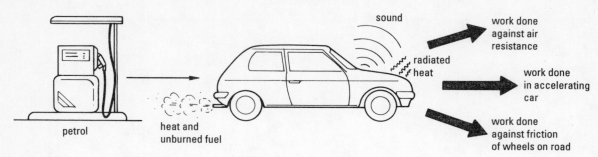

E5 The heat energy wasted in energy transfers can be reduced by:

- insulating the transducer
- reducing friction in the transducer
- capturing the heat energy and using it. ❏

E6 A **joulemeter** can be used to measure the energy used by electrical appliances. Domestic electricity meters act as joulemeters. ❏

E7 The **specific heat (thermal) capacity** of a substance is the amount of energy required to raise the temperature of 1 kg of the substance by 1 degree Celsius. The specific heat capacity of water is 4200 joules per kilogram per degree Celsius.

The energy transferred by heating can be found by using this formula:

energy transferred	=	mass of substance	×	specific heat capacity	×	rise in temperature
E (J)	=	m (kg)	×	s	×	Δt (°C)	❏

Rearrange the formula given above to show how to calculate a) the temperature rise and b) the mass of substance heated.

$t =$ $m =$

E8 If a heating device like a kettle is thermally insulated the efficiency of energy transfer will be closer to 100%.

To calculate the temperature rise of 2.5 kg of water in a 2.5 kW tea-urn in 2 minutes:

energy transferred = 2500 joules/second or 2500 × 120 joules in 2 minutes

$$\Delta t = \frac{E}{ms} \quad \text{or} \quad \Delta t = \frac{2500 \times 120}{2.5 \times 4200}$$

$$= 28.6 \,°C \qquad ❏$$

Calculate the mass of water whose temperature could be raised by 10 °C in 5 minutes in the tea-urn described on the left.

E9 When work is done by lifting an object against gravity there is always an increase in **potential energy**. The potential energy of an object depends on the mass of the object (m), the gravity force acting on it (g) and the height it is moved (h).

Energy transferred as potential energy, $E = mgh$ ❏

A 0.5 kg tub of margarine is moved from the floor to a shelf in the fridge 0.5 m higher up. Calculate the potential energy of the tub of margarine.

E10 The energy of a moving object depends on its mass and velocity. These are related by the formula:

$E = \frac{1}{2}mv^2$ where E = kinetic energy (J), m = mass (kg) and v = velocity (m/s). ❏

E11 A falling object loses potential energy and gains kinetic energy.

potential energy lost = kinetic energy gained or $mgh = \frac{1}{2}mv^2$

This can be rearranged to give $v^2 = 2gh$ or $v = \sqrt{(2gh)}$ and allows the velocity of the object at any point in its fall to be calculated. ❏

Calculate:
a) the potential energy of a 2.5 kg book on a shelf 2 m high

b) the kinetic energy of the book when it just hits the ground

c) the velocity of the book when it has fallen 1 m.

F1 Many large atoms are radioactive. A radioactive sample becomes less active (**decays**) with time. **Half-life** is the time taken for half of the nuclei to decay. ❏

Complete this graph to show how the count-rate of the radioisotope ^{14}C changes with time. (The half-life of ^{14}C is 5600 years.)

Initial count rate = 100 cpm (counts per minute)

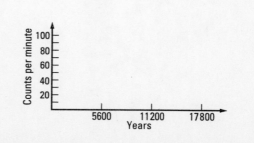

F2 Isotopes with a short half-life can be used in medicine because they decay quickly and therefore soon disappear from the body. Isotopes with medium half-lives are useful in industry. Isotopes with long, and very long half-lives can be used to date ancient objects and even rocks. ❏

Rearrange the following sentences by writing the letters in the correct boxes below to explain how ^{14}C can be used to date specimens that were once living.

a)   The isotope decays by β emission at a known rate.

b)   The level of ^{14}C in the body of an organism remains constant while it is alive.

c) ^{14}C is made constantly in the atmosphere by the action of neutrons on ^{14}N.

d)   The count-rate gradually reduces over time.

e) ^{14}C is expelled from the body during respiration.

f)   This replaces that lost by decay and the amount of ^{14}C in the atmosphere remains constant.

g) ^{14}C is taken into the body in food (or through photosynthesis).

h)   From the present count-rate the time when the organism stopped respiring can be estimated.

i)   After death the ^{14}C that decays is no longer replaced.

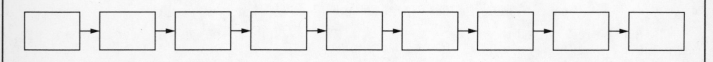

F3 Radioactive decay can be described by **nuclear equations**. A correct nuclear equation will show the type of radiation, the decay products and also account for all the protons and neutrons. The example below shows uranium-238 decaying by alpha emission. A nucleus of thorium-234 is produced. ❏

Check that all the protons and neutrons are accounted for in this nuclear equation by adding up the atomic numbers and the mass numbers on each side of the arrow.

$$^{238}_{92}U \rightarrow {}^{4}_{2}\alpha + {}^{234}_{90}Th$$

Write nuclear equations for the formation of ^{14}C in the atmosphere and also for its decay by β emission.

Answers

ANSWERS

Sc1 Foundation (pages 2–7)

Sc1 encourages investigation, and as a result there can be several correct responses to a question. The answers to Sc1 are a guide only.

A1

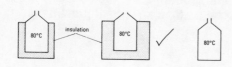

A2 1 **wool**   2 **fur**.   Or anything suitable.

A3 **Using equal quantities of dough in identical containers, place one container in a controlled temperature area of 35 °C, and one container in an identical area at a different temperature. Use a ruler to measure the height the dough rises over a defined period of time. Different temperatures above and below 35 °C should be tested, each time using a control.**

A4 Type of food supply: **proteins, fats, carbohydrates**
Amount of water: **more than 50 litres/day (including washing and toilet)**
Temperature: **0 °C–35 °C (internal 37 °C)**
Climate: **no extreme conditions**
Other factors: **social structure**
Shelter: **to protect from harsh weather, predators, etc.**

A5 **There would be fizzing around the chalk, which would dissolve, leaving a colourless solution.**

A6 **temperature   size of chalk pieces.**

A7 **34 °C; 40 °C.**

A8

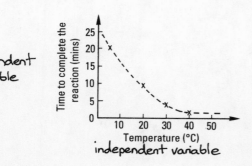

dependent variable
independent variable

A9 2   6   3
     1   4   5

**A10 concentration of acid   size of chalk particles
      temperature   type of container.**

A11

beakers contain 1 mol dm⁻³ acid
lump chalk
powdered chalk

C2

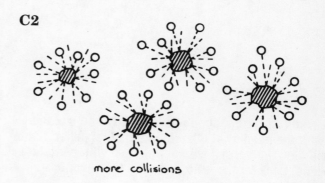

more collisions

rate would increase

C3 **smell; feel; sound.** Or anything suitable.

C4 **mass; width; density.** Or anything suitable.

C5 **The woollen cover is a good insulator. The nylon cover is not a good insulator.**

C6

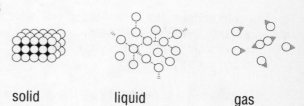

solid   liquid   gas

C7

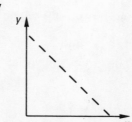

C8 **As the thickness of the insulator increases, its insulation effect increases.**

Wool is the best insulator, followed by cotton, rayon and nylon in descending order of effectiveness.

The temperature decreased over time.

D1 a) ★★★   b) ★   c) ★★   d) ★.

© JOHN MURRAY

137

Sc1 Higher (pages 8–14)

A1 That inheritance depends on the combination of two alleles, which are either double recessive, double dominant or heterozygous for a character; and that inheritance is in the ratio of 3 : 1. (Mendel's First Law).

A3

A4 atom   ion   pH.

A5 Investigate parent populations of *WW* and *ww* and count the number of offspring in the first generation, and then the second with normal and with miniature wings. Look for the ratio 1 : 2 : 1 in the second generation.

A6 The control plant should be grown in exactly the same conditions as the plants in the greenhouse. Each batch of plants in the greenhouse should be exposed to a change in one variable, for example temperature, moisture, light, carbon dioxide concentration. Indications of growth could be height increase of the plant, increased foliage, or increased dry weight.

A7 Remove a panel of glass to cool the greenhouse; add a heater to heat the greenhouse. Use an accurate thermometer for measurements. (Refer to D1, page 12 if necessary.)

A8 Any plan that uses a large sample size, a comparison between a control and an experimental group and a measurement of 'ill health'.

B1 amount of corrosion at temperatures in the range 25–250 °C.

B3 For example, by defining the age group and social group of the sample.

B4 height of a pot plant ╲   ╱ micrometer

height of a fir tree ╲ ╳ ╱ 30 cm ruler

length of a leaf ╱ ╳ ╲ metre stick

thickness of a leaf ╱   ╲ 10 m tape

C3 living cells contain water
sickle-cell anaemia is inherited.

C4 Aluminium corrodes in very acidic conditions, and in weakly acidic conditions.

D2 Lack of fine discrimination in instruments. Not carrying out a fair test. Not planning an experiment sufficiently before beginning. (The experimenter.)

D3 Effects of chemical pollution on health; transmission of disease from other species to humans. Or anything suitable.

D4 Readers were not sampled. Instead they chose whether or not to take part. Only a small number did so. Health problems were to be identified by the person rather than a medical practitioner.

D5 pH 3

D6 a) 1 in 4   b) 1 in 1000   c) 1 in 10   d) 1 in 1. Or suitable individual answers.

Sc2 Foundation (pages 16–38)

A2 animal cells:

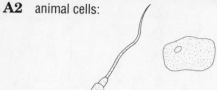

plant cells:

A3 cell membrane   cytoplasm   nucleus
chloroplasts   vacuole   cell wall

A4

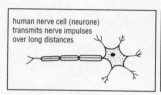

	Cell structure
human nerve cell (neurone) transmits nerve impulses over long distances	long cell covered in insulating materials with many connections to transmit nerve impulses

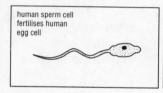

human sperm cell fertilises human egg cell	head carrying genetic information / tail for swimming

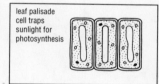

leaf palisade cell traps sunlight for photosynthesis	Long cells with large surface area / many chloroplasts to trap light

A5

tissue — a group of cells with the same structure and function

organ — a structure, made up of several different tissues, which carries out one particular function.

system — a group of organs and tissues carrying out one life process

A6

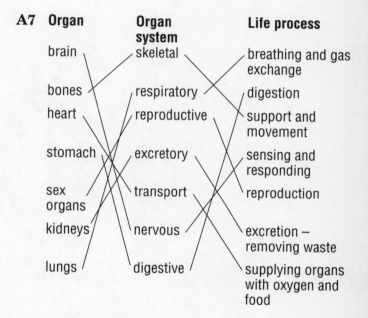

A7

Organ	Organ system	Life process
brain	skeletal	breathing and gas exchange
bones	respiratory	digestion
heart	reproductive	support and movement
stomach	excretory	sensing and responding
sex organs	transport	reproduction
kidneys	nervous	excretion – removing waste
lungs	digestive	supplying organs with oxygen and food

A8
1 **heart; arteries**
2 **support; protect**
3 **digestion**
4 **kidneys**
5 **brain; nerves**
6 **lungs; oxygen**
7 **ovaries; sperm**

A9

enable the plant to reproduce — flower, stamens

carry out photosynthesis — leaves

support leaves and flowers — stem

anchor plant in soil — roots

ovary

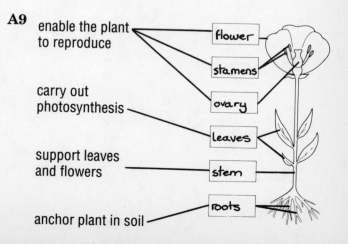

A10

Life processes	Animals and plants	Plants only	Animals only
• gas exchange	✓		
• reproduction	✓		
• responding to the environment	✓		
• transport	✓		
• excretion	✓		
• movement			✓
• digestion			✓
• photosynthesis		✓	

B2

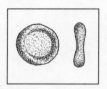

structure: liver, gall bladder

structure: pancreas

what happens: produces enzymes

structure	what happens
mouth	chew food some digestion
gullet (oesophagus)	pass food to stomach - peristalsis
stomach	churn food and chemical digestion
small intestine	chemical digestion
large intestine	absorbs water
anus	egest waste

B3
starch → glucose
protein → amino acids
fat → fatty acids and glycerol

B4
pepsin
amylases, proteases, lipases

B6

right side — to lungs; left side — to body

artery; artery

from body; from lungs

vein; vein

right atrium; left atrium

blue; red

right ventricle; left ventricle

muscle

B7
See labelled diagram of heart in answer to B6 for position of arteries and veins.

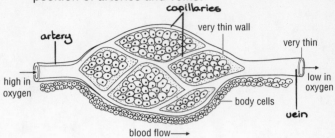

artery — high in oxygen; capillaries; very thin wall; very thin — low in oxygen; vein; body cells; blood flow →

B8

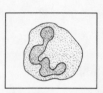

Red blood cells carry oxygen to body cells.

White blood cells attack microbes or produce antibodies.

Platelets help form a blood clot.

Plasma liquid carries digested food, carbon dioxide, antibodies.

B9
oxygen; carbon dioxide

B10
inhaled; exhaled

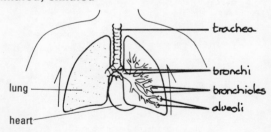

trachea; bronchi; bronchioles; alveoli; lung; heart

B11
receptors: eyes, ears, skin, tongue, nose, inner ear
stimuli: light, sound, pressure, chemicals, chemicals, gravity

B12
stimulus → receptor → co-ordinator →
heat from fire   heat receptors   brain
                  in leg

effector → response
leg muscles   move leg away
               from heat

B13

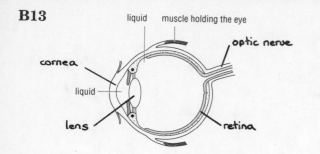

liquid · muscle holding the eye · optic nerve · cornea · liquid · lens · retina

B14

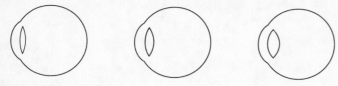

B15

Dim light · Normal light · Bright light

B16

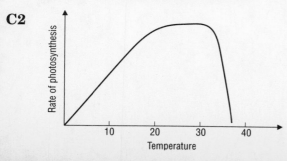

pituitary · thyroid · adrenal · pancreas · sex organs

B17 Gain water by **drinking, food**
Lose water by **urine, faeces, sweating**

B18 Kidneys reabsorb a lot of water.
Small amount of concentrated urine produced.

C1 carbon dioxide + water → glucose + oxygen
use as energy source; store as starch; use to make
cellulose and other growth materials

C2

Rate of photosynthesis vs Temperature (10, 20, 30, 40)

C3 glucose + oxygen $\xrightarrow{\text{energy released}}$ carbon dioxide + water

C4
Potassium — required for formation of chlorophyll for photosynthesis
Nitrogen — required for formation of proteins and genetic material
Phosphorus — required at rapidly growing parts of plant – leaves and fruit
Magnesium — required for energy-requiring reactions and genetic material

C5

C7 daytime gas exchange; night-time gas exchange

C8

Factor	Effect on transpiration rate
High temperature	**increase**
Low humidity	**increase**
Still air	**decrease**

D5

Cause of variation	
both parents short	**genetic**
mother smoked during pregnancy	**environmental**
mother ate healthy diet while pregnant	**environmental**
low light intensity	**environmental**
acid soil	**environmental**
parent plants tall	**genetic**

D6 mother XX · father XY
mother's sex cells X or X · father's sex cells X or Y

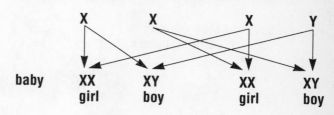

X   X   X   Y

baby   XX   XY   XX   XY
       girl   **boy**   **girl**   **boy**

D8

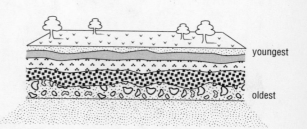

youngest · oldest

E1 light; space/mates; water

E2 a) **water gain**
b) **absorb**
c) **external**
d) **streamlined**
e) **reduced**

E3 **large** area of roots to absorb any available water
small surface area of leaves to prevent water loss
large amount of water-storing tissue

E4

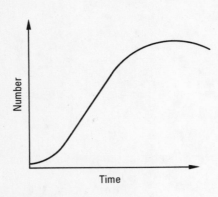

E5 **air; soil; water**
car exhausts; factory smoke; used nuclear reactor fuel; etc.

E7 obtaining and burning
burning fossil fuels

producing food

over-use of fertilisers causing water pollution

formation of spoil tips causing land pollution

release of greenhouse gases and creation of acid rain

destruction of habitats for farmland

E9 producers: **grass; pondweed**
consumers: **other members of chains**

herbivores:

carnivores:

E11 less; decrease; less; increase; herbivores

E15

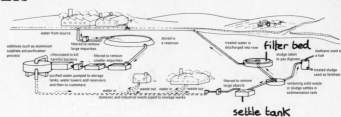

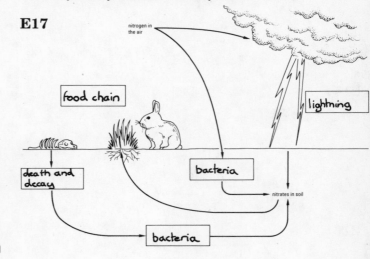

E16 1 **photosynthesis**   2 **respiration**

E17

Sc2 Higher (pages 39–52)

A1

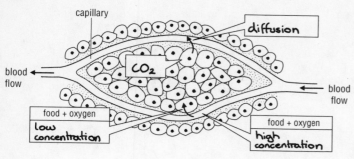

A2

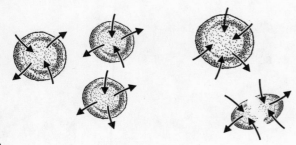

A3

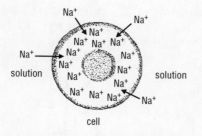

A5 **growth; reproduction; half the full number of chromosomes**

A6

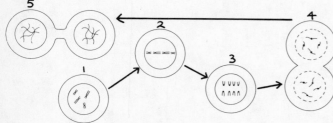

B1

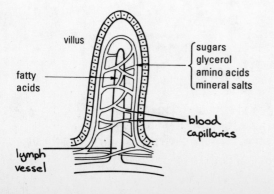

B2 **exhaling; inhaling**

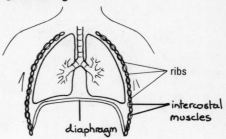

B6 sex hormone — diabetes, control of blood sugar level

growth hormone — promoting human growth

insulin — controlling and promoting fertility

B7

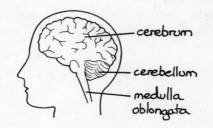

B8

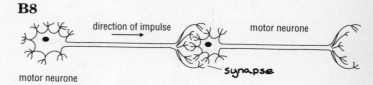

sensor → sensory neurone →
brain → motor neurone → effector muscle

B9 **Touch an object and withdraw hand.
Shield eyes from bright Sun.
Put hands out when falling.
Duck when there is a loud crash.**

B11

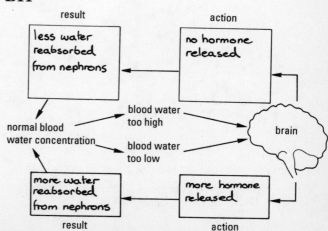

ANSWERS

B12

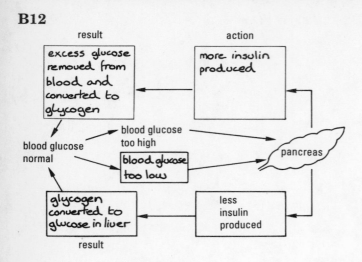

B13 Stage 1: **liquid forced from blood capillaries into Bowman's capsule.**
Stage 2: **water, mineral salts reabsorbed from kidney tubule into blood capillaries.**

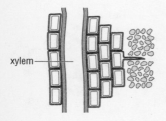

B14 When blood pH falls the breathing rate **increases**.
When blood pH rises the breathing rate **decreases**.

B15 Metabolic rate decreases, no shivering, blood diverted to surface vessels and body hairs lowered, sweating begins.

C1

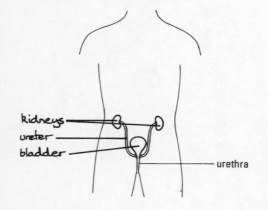

Water concentration in root hair cell is greater than water concentration in cell 1 so water moves into cell from root hair cell 1 by osmosis.

D2

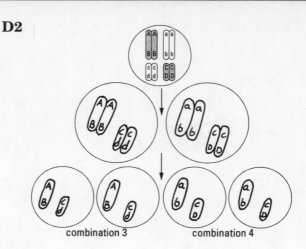

D6 male Ss x ss female

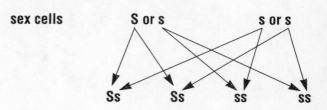

sex cells   S or s   s or s

Ss   Ss   ss   ss

genotypic ratio   **2 heterozygous: 2 homozygous recessive or 1 : 1**
phenotypic ratio   **equal numbers of straight-winged and curly-winged flies**

D9

D11

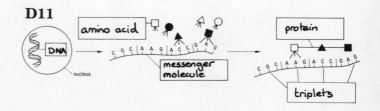

D12 breeds of cats and dogs
breeding for milk yield in cattle
breeding for new varieties of apples, potatoes etc.

D14 1 **bacterial DNA**
2 **human insulin gene**
3 **clones**
4 **extraction and purification**

D16 darker moths selected **for**
darker moths selected **against**

E1 deforestation   atmosphere ——— • global warming

soil —— • organisms must
adapt to
organisms   environmental
changes

• soil erosion

greenhouse   atmosphere • habitats
gases from   destroyed
burning fossil   organisms • less
fuels   photosynthesis
so more CO_2,
less O_2

release of   atmosphere • UV rays damage
CFC gases   skin, for example
organisms   cancers

• ozone layer
damaged

E7 removing hedges to
increase area of fields,
making ploughing and
harvesting easier

rapid spread of disease
or pests

destruction of habitats

adding fertilisers to the
soil using insecticides

fertilisers leached from
soil into waterways
causing pollution

using insecticides to kill
pests

poisons pass into food
chains and are
concentrated along
chain

growing same plants in
huge areas (monoculture)

E3

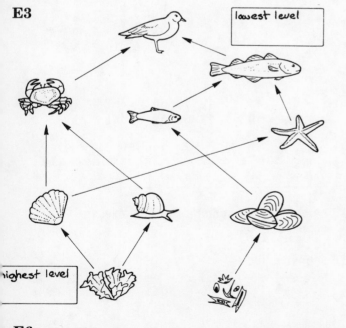

lowest level

highest level

E6

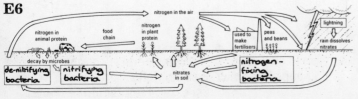

Sc3 Foundation (pages 54–73)

A1

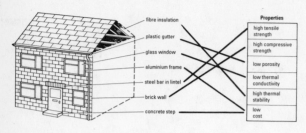

A2 Solids: **wood**   **stone**   Liquids: **milk**   **water**
Gases: **nitrogen**   **carbon dioxide.**

A3

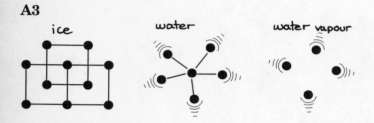

A4 0 °C   100 °C

A5

A7

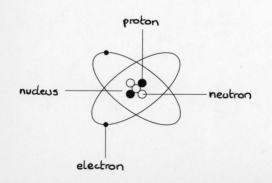

A8

A9 $_6$C: **6** protons
          6 electrons

  $_{11}$Na: **11** protons
          11 electrons

  $_{12}$Mg: **12** protons
          12 electrons

  $_{17}$Cl: **17** protons
          17 electrons

A10

Symbol	Number of protons	Number of electrons	Number of neutrons
$^{27}_{13}$Al	**13**	**13**	**14**
$^{19}_{9}$F	**9**	**9**	**10**
$^{197}_{79}$Au	**79**	**79**	**118**

A11 ^{12}C: $p = 6$; $n = 6$; $e = 6$
    ^{14}C: $p = 6$; $n = 8$; $e = 6$

A12 The outer shell determines the chemical behaviour. It interacts with electrons of other atoms.

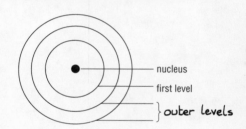

A13

	Na$^+$	Mg^{2+}	F$^-$	O^{2-}
protons	**11**	**12**	**9**	**8**
electrons	**10**	**10**	**10**	**10**

A14

Group	1	2	3	4	5	6	7	8
Valency	1	2	3	4	3	2	**1**	**0**

**A15 carbon; four   sodium; chlorine; oxygen
copper sulphate.**

A16 sodium oxide

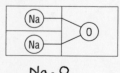

Na$_2$O

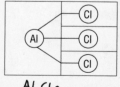

Al Cl$_3$

A17 Ionic compounds: **sodium chlorate; copper nitride; copper nitrate; copper sulphate**
Covalent compounds: **carbon tetrachloride; carbon dioxide; sulphur trioxide.**

A18 low   do not conduct.

B1

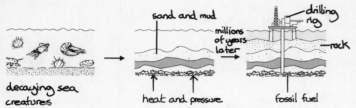

decaying sea creatures → heat and pressure → fossil fuel

sand and mud — millions of years later — drilling rig — rock

B2

less useful molecules ← reforming • change structure

crude oil → distillation • heat • boil • condense → small useful molecules gas petrol kerosine → cracking • break → big molecules oil tar → some unsaturated molecules → polymerisation • make → plastics

B3 **Petrol, kerosene, fuel oil**, etc.

B5
CO_2	acid rain
CO	brain damage
NO_2	greenhouse gas
lead compounds	poisonous

B6 Alkenes are unsaturated hydrocarbons because they have **a double C═C covalent bond.**

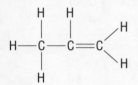

B7

B11

K, Na, Li, Ca, Mg, Al	**melting and then electrolysis**
Zn, Fe, Sn, Pb	**heating with carbon**
Cu, Hg	**strong heating**
Ag, Pt, Au	**gentle heating/chemical methods**

B12 copper   nickel   iron.

B13 copper **bulb lights**   magnesium **bulb lights**
sulphur **bulb does not light**   Ag **bulb lights**
Ar **bulb does not light**   Al **bulb lights.**

B14 malleable – **able to be beaten, rolled, etc. into a new shape**
ductile – **able to be drawn out into wire without breaking**
high tensile strength – **able to be stretched considerably without breaking.**

B16 **gold ring, glass vase, slate roof, petrol, marble column,** etc.

B17 **copper; iron   crystal glass; soda glass polyethene; polystyrene   brick; china cotton; flax.**

B18

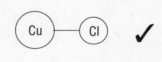

Cu — Cl ✓

B7

	with water	with acid	with chlorine	with oxygen
K Na Li Ca	displace hydrogen gas from cold water	violent explosive reaction	combine very energetically with chlorine to form stable ionic chloride salts	
Mg Al Zn Fe Sn	only displace hydrogen from steam	displace hydrogen from acid		
Pb Cu Hg Au Pt	do not displace hydrogen from water or steam	do not displace hydrogen from acid	combine slowly to form unstable salts	

colour key

■ give out a lot of energy   ▨ give out some energy   □ do not release any energy

B20

ammonium   sulphate

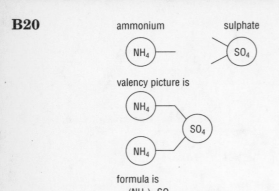

valency picture is

formula is
(NH$_4$)$_2$ SO$_4$

B21 sodium oxide

Na $\times$ O
1   2
Na$_2$O

hydrogen fluoride

H $\times$ F
1   1
HF

magnesium chloride

Mg $\times$ Cl
2   1
MgCl$_2$

silver(I) sulphide

Ag $\times$ S
1   2
Ag$_2$S

iron(II) chloride

Fe $\times$ Cl
2   1
FeCl$_2$

lithium nitrate

Li $\times$ NO$_3$
1   1
LiNO$_3$

aluminium phosphate

Al $\times$ PO$_4$
3   3
AlPO$_4$

calcium hydroxide

Ca $\times$ OH
2   1
Ca(OH)$_2$

ammonium carbonate

NH$_4$ $\times$ CO$_3$
1   2
(NH$_4$)$_2$CO$_3$

B23 copper oxide   sulphur   calcium + oxygen
carbon dioxide + water   oxygen; carbon dioxide.

B24 hydrochloric acid + calcium carbonate → calcium chloride + carbon dioxide + water

HCl		CaCO$_3$	CaCl$_2$	CO$_2$	H$_2$O
2HCl	+	CaCO$_3$	→ CaCl$_2$	+ CO$_2$	+ H$_2$O
2HCl(aq)	+	CaCO$_3$(s)	→ CaCl$_2$(aq)	+ CO$_2$(g)	+ H$_2$O(l)

copper oxide + carbon → copper + carbon dioxide

CuO   C   Cu   CO$_2$
2CuO   +   C   →   2Cu   +   CO$_2$
2CuO(s)   +   C(s)   →   2Cu(s)   +   CO$_2$(g)

methane   +   oxygen   →   carbon dioxide   +   water

CH$_4$ O$_2$ CO$_2$ H$_2$O
CH$_4$ +   2O$_2$ →   CO$_2$ +   2H$_2$O
CH$_4$(g)   +   2O$_2$(g)   →   CO$_2$(g)   +   2H$_2$O(l)

B25

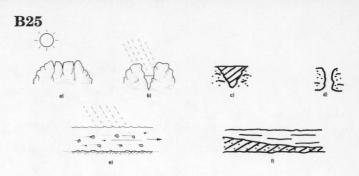

a)   b)   c)   d)

e)   f)

B26 calcite; fluorite; iron pyrites.

B27 igneous: **basalt, granite**   sedimentary: **sandstone, shale**   metamorphic: **marble, slate.**

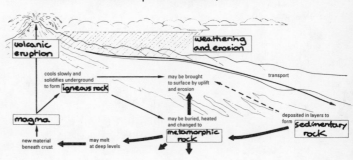

B28 Limestone: **sediment, including dead creatures, settled. Everything was squashed and became rock. Some of the creatures had shells, which became limestone.**
Granite: **molten magma cooled slowly to form an igneous rock with large crystals – granite.**
Marble: **limestone was heated quickly underground and changed to the metamorphic rock – marble. All the shells were destroyed by heat and pressure.**

B29

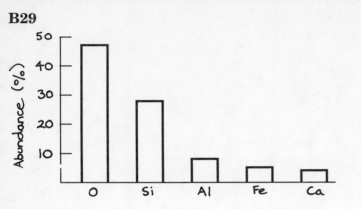

C1

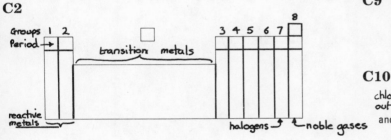

most common non-metal: oxygen   most common metal: aluminium

C2

Groups 1 2
Period
transition metals
3 4 5 6 7
8
reactive metals
halogens   noble gases

C4 F: **pale greenish-yellow; least dense; very reactive; displaces Cl, Br, I.**

Cl: **greenish-yellow; denser than F; reactive; displaces Br, I.**

Br: **dark red; denser than Cl; less reactive; displaces I.**

I: **black; most dense; much less reactive; is displaced by others.**

C5 a) **Helium**   **All colourless**
b) **Neon**
c) **Argon**
d) **Krypton**
e) **Xenon**
f) **Radon**

C6

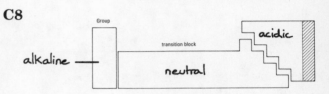

C7 Alkali metal + oxygen → **metal oxide**

Alkali metal + chlorine → **metal chloride**

C8

Group

alkaline

transition block

acidic

neutral

C9 Element A is **chlorine**.
Element B is **fluorine**.
Element C is **bromine**.
The group name is **the halogens**.

C10

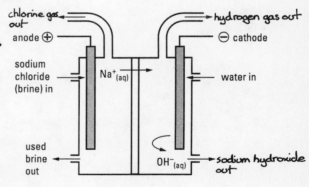

chlorine gas out
anode ⊕
sodium chloride (brine) in
Na⁺(aq)
used brine out
OH⁻(aq)
hydrogen gas out
⊖ cathode
water in
sodium hydroxide out

C11 Cost of process: electricity, **workforce, apparatus**

Product	Sold to make	Benefits	Drawbacks
chlorine	pesticides	increased crop yields	toxic to environment
	PVC	long lasting	non-biodegradable
	bleach	kills all germs	toxic
	clean water	reduced disease	smell, taste
hydrogen	margarine	substitute to butter	still fattening
	hydrochloric acid	widely used in industry	toxic, acidic
sodium hydroxide	paper	communication	loss of trees
	soaps/ detergents	cleanse	pollution
	synthetic materials	ease life	non-biodegradable

C12 Iron – make steel for buildings
Copper – electrical wires
Silver – precious metal
Chromium – alloys
etc.

C13 Blue – **copper(II) ion;**
purple – **manganate(VII) ion (permanganate);**
yellow – **chromate(VI) ion (chromate)**

C14 slow – **rusting**
quick – **burning**

C15

increase   decrease   decrease

C16 increased temperature — more particles, so more collisions

decreased particle size of reactants — more energy to activate more successful collisions

catalyst present — more particles touching so more collisions

increased concentration of reactants — particles better positioned so more successful collisions

C17 boiling potatoes; cooking toast
cutting up vegetables before cooking
rennin when making cheese
adding fresh coal to a dying fire.

C18

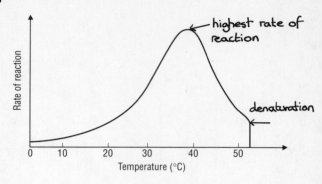

C19 Haber process: nitrogen gas and hydrogen gas react to make ammonia. Gases passed over an iron catalyst.

Cement manufacture: limestone and shale ground into small pieces. Heated in a kiln.

Oxyacetylene torch: acetylene is burned in a high concentration of oxygen to give greater heat.

C20

endothermic   exothermic   exothermic   exothermic

C21 heat; carbon dioxide.

Sc3 Higher (pages 74–91)

A1 35.5 amu

A2 $A_r = \dfrac{(20 \times 90) + (22 \times 10)}{100}$

$= 20.2$ amu

A3 hydrogen oxide H_2O (1)2 + 16 = 18 amu
sodium fluoride NaF 23 + 19 = 42 amu
calcium carbonate $CaCO_3$
40 + 12 + (16)3 = 100 amu

A4
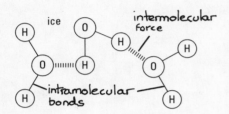
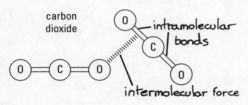

A7
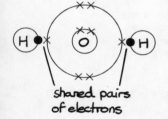
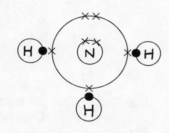

A8
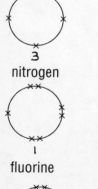
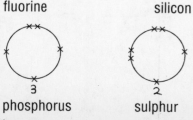

A9
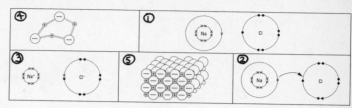

A10

	Metal						Non-metal
Group	1	2	3	4	5	6	7
Electrons in outer shell	1	2	3	4	5	6	7
To become stable	lose 1	2	3	gain 3	2	1	
Ion formed	+	2+	3+	3–	2–	–	
Example	Na^+	Mg^{2+}	Al^{3+}	N^{3-}	S^{2-}	F^-	

A12
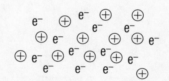

copper

sodium chloride

glucose

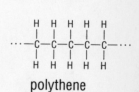

diamond

graphite

polythene

A14 SiO_2

A15
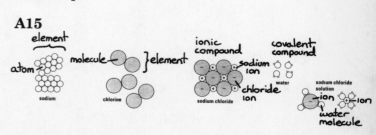

A16 oxygen gas and copper metal
oxygen gas and hydrogen gas.

A17

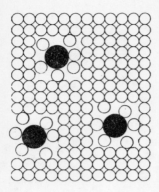

B1

first in series	**ethene**
molecular formula	C_2H_4
structural formula	

$$\begin{array}{ccc} H & & H \\ \ & C = C & / \\ / & & \ \\ H & & H \end{array}$$

general formula for the series	C_nH_{2n}
trend in physical properties	**boiling point and viscosity increase as molecules get bigger**
chemical properties	**small ones burn well; decolorise bromine water very fast; double C═C bonds so reactive**

B2

heptane
C_7H_{16}

↓

pentane
C_5H_{12}

+

ethene
C_2H_4

B3

addition polymers: **polypropene; polyvinylchloride; polyethene**
Polypropene – plastic bags; polyvinylchloride – waterproof coat; polyethene – plastic bags

B4

thermal stability:	**very high**
thermal conductivity:	**low**
boiling point:	**above 2500 °C**
solubility in water:	**zero**
compression strength:	**very high**
thermoplasticity:	**zero**
biodegradability:	**zero**

B5

No cross-linking: **ductile; weak in compression and tension; low melting and boiling points; malleable; soft**
Lots of cross-linking: **brittle; stronger in compression and tension; higher melting and boiling points; hard.**

B6

Metal	Reactivity	Extraction
sodium, aluminium	very reactive	electrolysis
iron	reactive	blast furnace
lead	less reactive	heat with carbon

B7

battery (d.c.)

impure tin — — pure tin

— solution containing tin ions

Sn²⁺

tin atoms oxidised to form ions

tin ions reduced to form atoms

B8 oxygen   water.

B9
1 **keep oxygen out (by using a fire extinguisher)**
2 **remove fuel (by chopping down trees in a forest)**
3 **lower the temperature (by using water).**

B10

showing electron pairs

B11

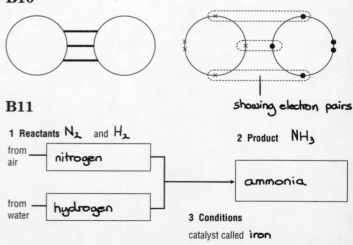

1 Reactants N_2 and H_2

2 Product NH_3

from air → nitrogen

from water → hydrogen

→ ammonia

3 Conditions

catalyst called **iron**

medium temperature of about **450°C**

medium pressure of about **200 atmospheres**

B12 b) ammonium nitrate, made by reacting ammonia with **nitric acid**.

c) ammonium phosphate, made by **reacting ammonia with phosphoric acid**.

B13 Fertiliser dissolves in rain water and is drained into streams and ponds and through the soil into our drinking water. In ponds and rivers the fertiliser helps algae to grow and multiply quickly. This is called eutrophication. These small organisms may colour the water green. They die, decay and the decomposer microbes then use up oxygen in the water so organisms suffocate. In drinking water the fertilisers are taken into our bodies. Such chemicals may cause cancer. They have also been known to interfere with blood cells so that the blood cannot carry enough oxygen. This results in blue baby syndrome.

B14

a) $g = 2 \times 100$
$= 200$ g

b) moles $= \dfrac{50}{100}$
$= 0.5$ mol

B16 2 moles of Na **need 16 g of oxygen to burn.**
10 moles of Na **need 80 g of oxygen to burn.**
46 g of Na **need 16 g of oxygen to burn.**
9.2 g of Na **need 3.2 g of oxygen to burn.**

B18

	Cu	O
Mass	0.87 g	0.11 g
A_r	64	16
Moles	0.0136	0.007
Formula	$Cu_{13.6}$	O_7
Approximately	Cu_2O	

B19 **30** cm^3 of oxygen   **15** cm^3 of carbon dioxide.

B20 $CaCO_3$ + $2HNO_3$ → $Ca(NO_3)_2$ + CO_2 + H_2O

1 mol   2 mol   1 mol   1 mol   1 mol

100 g   126 g   164 g   44 g   18 g

If 50 g calcium carbonate react, then 22 g carbon dioxide are produced.

B21 $\frac{1}{2}$ **mole, therefore 12.5 litres.**

B22 electrons on left = gain = reduction
electrons on right = loss = oxidation
**oxidation; oxidation; reduction;
reduction; reduction; reduction**

B23 At the negative electrode: **each copper ion gains two electrons and becomes a neutral copper atom.**
At the positive electrode: **each chloride ion loses an electron. Two neutral chlorine atoms join to make a chlorine molecule.**

B26 *Q:* charge, in coulombs

I: current (i.e. passage of electrons), in amperes

t: time, in seconds.

B28

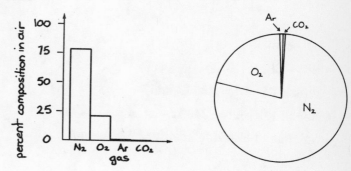

B29 oxygen   nitrogen   water vapour.

B30

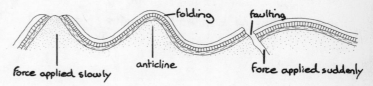

B31

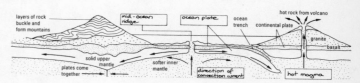

B32 plates slide past one another

plates collide and crumple at the edges

plates separate as new material is extruded

fold mountains and trenches

mid-ocean ridges

fault lines which are susceptible to earthquakes

C1 $_4$Be   4   2,2

$_{12}$Mg   12   2,8,2

$_{20}$Ca   20   2,8,8,2

C2

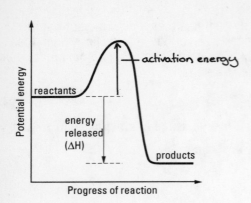

C4 Reactants:

$H_2 + Cl_2$

break 1 H—H = 436 kJ/mol

break 1 Cl—Cl = 243 kJ/mol

total bond-breaking energy = 679 kJ/mol

Products:

2HCl

make 2 H—Cl = 2(431) = 862 kJ/mol

total bond-making energy = 862 kJ/mol

overall energy = energy in − energy out
=   679   −   862
= −183 kJ/mol.

C5

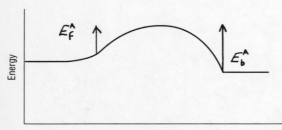

C6 Number **1** is reversible.
High yield by:
1 removing NH$_3$(g) as it forms (by cooling)
2 using a high pressure
**3 using a moderate temperature, which speeds up
the reaction without destroying the ammonia.**

C7 $2SO_2 + O_2 \rightleftharpoons 2SO_3$ **Contact process**
$N_2 + 3H_2 \rightleftharpoons 2NH_3$ **Haber process**

Sc4 Foundation (pages 94–120)

A1

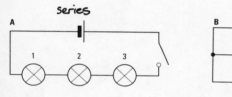

transfers electrical energy into light (and heat) energy

conducts electrical charges around a circuit

provides the energy to push the electrical charges round a circuit

opens or closes a circuit to stop or start the flow of electric charge

reduces the electric current by a fixed amount

varies the size of electric current as it is adjusted

a switch turned on or off by an electric current

A2

series   parallel

In circuit A: **open – no bulb lights up; closed – all three bulbs light.**
In circuit B: **open – bulbs 2 and 3 light; closed – all three bulbs light.**

A3

In circuit A: **bulbs 2 and 3 do not light.**
In circuit B: **bulbs 2 and 3 light.**

A4

Low resistance	High resistance
short	**long**
thick	**thin**
copper	**light bulb filament**

A5

electric fire, hair dryer, light bulb, electric cooker, electric blanket, etc.

A8

a cell; a bulb; lowering voltage of cell; adding a bulb

A9

A2 **0.3**; A3 **0.3**   A2 **0.2**; A3 **0.1**.

A10

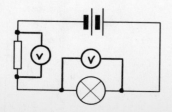

A11

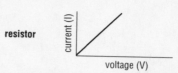

resistor

As *V* increases *I* increases at the same rate.

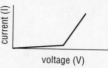

diode

**As *V* increases *I* increases slowly at first.
At a certain point *I* increases at a faster rate.**

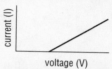

thermistor

**As *V* increases there is no increase in *I* at first.
At a certain point *I* increases rapidly.**

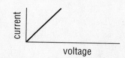

bulb

As *V* increases *I* increases at the same rate.

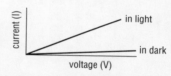

light dependent resistor (LDR)

As *V* increases *I* increases at the same rate in light but in dark as *V* increases very slowly

A12

a) **9 units × 2 hours × 8p = £1.44**
b) **2 × 0.1 units × 10 hours × 8p = 16p**

A14

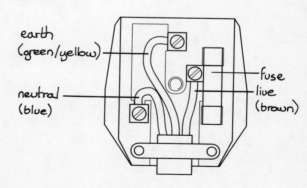

earth (green/yellow)

neutral (blue)

fuse

live (brown)

A16

$$current = \frac{100}{230} = 0.435 \quad \text{so use a 3 amp fuse}$$

$$current = \frac{2000}{230} = 8.695 \quad \text{so use a 13 amp fuse}$$

A17

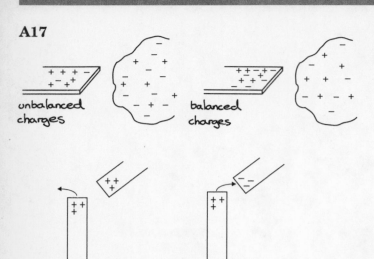

unbalanced charges

balanced charges

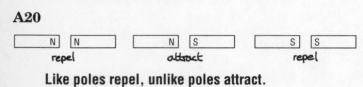

A18
1 **lightning**
2 **removal of acrylic pullover, touching a television screen or anything suitable**

A20

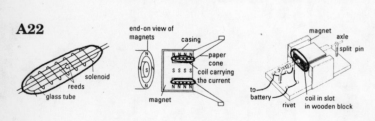

repel   attract   repel

Like poles repel, unlike poles attract.

A21

more current flowing

soft iron core

increased number of coils in wire

A22

end-on view of magnets

casing

paper cone

coil carrying the current

solenoid

reeds

glass tube

magnet

magnet

axle

split pin

to battery

rivet

coil in slot in wooden block

A24

N

S

A

A25

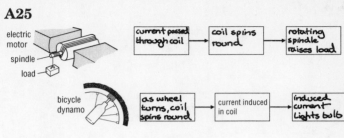

electric motor

spindle

load

| current passed through coil | → | coil spins round | → | rotating spindle raises load |

bicycle dynamo

| as wheel turns, coil spins round | → | current induced in coil | → | induced current lights bulb |

B2

pushing	pushing
squashing	pulling
pulling	tearing
twisting	pulling

B4
bending; pushing/squashing; pulling

B5

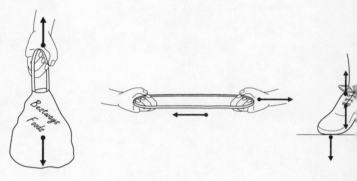

Bestways Foods

B6

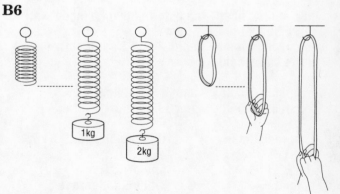

1kg

2kg

B8
accelerate; change direction; decelerate

B9
$t = s/v$; $s = v \times t$; **80 km/h**

B10

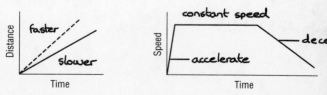

Distance

faster

slower

Time

Speed

constant speed

dece

accelerate

Time

B11 Increases stopping distance   Decreases stopping distance

faster speed   drier road
smoother road surface   deeper tyre tread

B12 acceleration = $\dfrac{\text{final velocity} - \text{starting velocity}}{\text{time taken}}$

acceleration = $\dfrac{12 - 0}{10}$ = 1.2 m/s²

B13 Force acting = 600 N   Force acting = 300 N

mass = 60 kg   mass = 30 kg

$a = F/m = 600/60$ $a = F/m = 300/30$

    = 10 m/s²   = 10 m/s²

B17

pressure = ~~force × area~~

pressure = ~~$\dfrac{\text{area}}{\text{force}}$~~

pressure = $\dfrac{\text{force}}{\text{area}}$ = $\dfrac{800}{0.3}$ = 2667 N/m²

C3

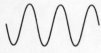
greater frequency

longer wavelength

smaller amplitude

C4

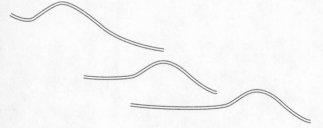

C6

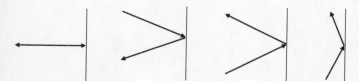

C7

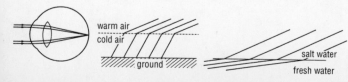
warm air
cold air
ground
salt water
fresh water

C10

UHF   microwaves   infrared   ultraviolet   X-rays

1000 m   1 m   0.001 m   0.000 001 m   0.000 000 001 m   0.000 000 000 001 m
1 km   1 mm   1µm   1 nm   0.001 nm

radio and TV waves   visible light   gamma rays

C11

Electromagnetic radiation	Use
radio waves	radio and TV transmission
microwaves	radio and TV transmission via satellite, radar, microwave ovens
infra-red	heating, cooking
visible light	seeing, photography
ultraviolet	sunbeds, skin treatment, killing bacteria
X-rays	X-rays and CT scanners
gamma rays	killing cancers

C12

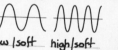
different pitch, same loudness
low/soft   high/soft

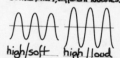
same pitch, different loudness
high/soft   high/loud

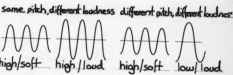
different pitch, different loudness
high/soft   low/loud

C13

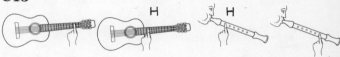

D1   Mercury   Venus   Earth   Mars   Jupiter
Saturn   Uranus   Neptune   Pluto

D2

day   night

summer in northern hemisphere   Sun   winter in northern hemisphere

D3   planet, Sun, solar system, galaxy, universe

D4   increases; decreases

D7

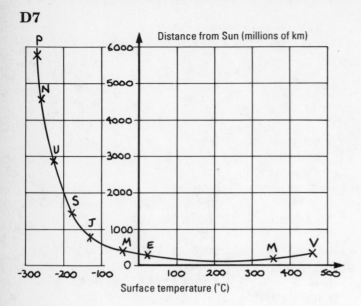

Distance from Sun (millions of km) / Surface temperature (°C)

D8

Inner: **Mercury; Venus; Earth; Mars**
Outer: **Jupiter; Saturn; Uranus; Neptune**

E1

1 **electrical; heat**
2 **light; chemical**
3 **radio, TV**
4 **bicycle dynamo**

E2

chemical; heat; stored; movement/kinetic; electrical

E3

1 *light + sound*
2 *heat*
3 sound + *heat*
4 **electrical** → kinetic + *heat*

E4

non-renewable	renewable
energy sources that will eventually run out	energy sources that are not used up
coal	**wind**
oil	**water**
gas	**waves**
nuclear fuel	**sunshine**

E5

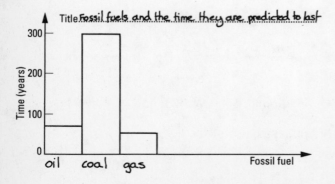

Title Fossil fuels and the time they are predicted to last

Time (years) / Fossil fuel / oil / coal / gas

E8

	Radiation	Convection	Conduction
Heat transfer through	**air or space**	liquids/gases	**solids, liquids, gases**
Heat transfer by	**vibrating particles transfer some of their heat energy in form of electromagnetic waves**	convection currents	passing vibrations through neighbouring particles in non-metals or free electrons in metals
One example	**heat from Sun to Earth**	local winds in weather system, water heating in a kettle	soldering iron

E10 conduction; convection; conduction

E11

work done = 5 N × 1.2 m = 6 joules
power = 6 joules/6 = 1 watt

E13

$I = P/V$
$V = P/I$
$P = 230 \times 9.6 = 2208$ watts
$P = 230 \times 12.5 = 2875$ watts
$I = P/V = 60/230 = 0.26$ amperes

F1

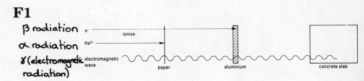

β radiation
α radiation   He²⁺
γ (electromagnetic radiation)   electromagnetic wave   paper   aluminium   concrete slab

F2 radiation from isotopes in air

F3 c, f, a, e, b, d

Sc4 Higher (pages 121–134)

A3 current, $I = V/R$
resistance, $R = V/I$
Current flowing: $I = V/R = 3/100 = 0.03$ **amperes**

A4 $R = 100 + 200 + 300$
$R = 600\ \Omega$
$1/R = 1/100 + 1/100 + 1/200 = 5/200$
$R = 200/5 = 40\ \Omega$

A5

Appliance	Power rating	Voltage	Current	Resistance
car headlamp	**36 watts**	12 volts	3 amperes	**4 Ω**
electric drill	240 watts	240 volts	**1 ampere**	**240 Ω**

A6 $I = Q/t$ $t = Q/I$

A7 $Q = I \times t = 4 \times (1.5 \times 60 \times 60) = 21\,600$ **coulombs**

A8

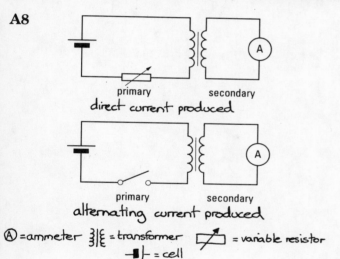

direct current produced

alternating current produced

Ⓐ = ammeter ⧙⧘ = transformer ▭ = variable resistor
⊣⊢ = cell

A9

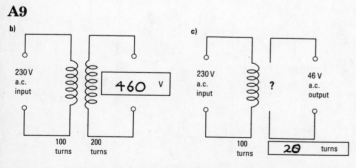

b)
230 V a.c. input — 100 turns — 200 turns — **460 V**

c)
230 V a.c. input — 100 turns — ? — **20** turns — 46 V a.c. output

When the voltage is stepped up the current is stepped **down** and vice versa.

A11

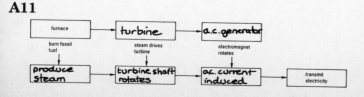

furnace → turbine → a.c. generator
burn fossil fuel / steam drives turbine / electromagnet rotates
produce steam → turbine shaft rotates → a.c. current induced → transmit electricity

B2

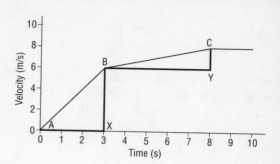

Gradient of line between B and C
$= CY/BY = 2/5 = 0.4\ \text{m/s}^2$
Total distance travelled = area of triangle BAX + area of triangle BCY + area of rectangle BYDX
$= 7.5 + 5 + 30 = 42.5$ m

B5 stopping force $= \dfrac{m\,(v - u)}{t}$

$= \dfrac{1000\,(0 - 10)}{0.1} = 100\,000$ N

stopping force $= \dfrac{m\,(v - u)}{t}$

$= \dfrac{1000\,(0 - 10)}{0.15} = 66\,667$ N

B6 Force at B $= \dfrac{\text{force at A} \times \text{area B}}{\text{area A}}$

$= \dfrac{5\,\text{N} \times 80\,\text{cm}^2}{5\,\text{cm}^2}$

$= 80\,\text{N}$

B7 $\dfrac{P_1 V_1}{T_1} = \dfrac{P_2 V_2}{T_2}$

$\dfrac{1 \times 4}{200} = \dfrac{3 \times y}{200}$

$y = \dfrac{200 \times 4}{200 \times 3}$

$y = 1.3$ litres

C1

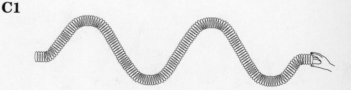

expansion   expansion
compression   compression   compression

C3 a) and b) **Because light (a) reflected from the cricket ball or (b) from the flash travels much faster than sound to a person standing at a distance.**

C4 wavelength = speed/frequency $\quad \lambda = v/f$
frequency = speed/wavelength $\quad f = v/\lambda$

C6

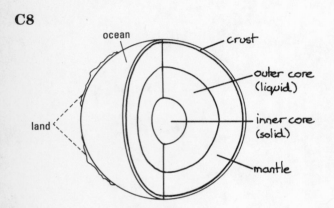

constructive interference

destructive interference

C8

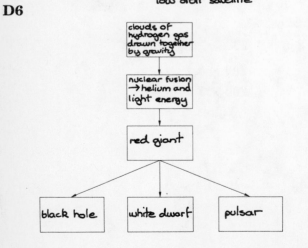

ocean — crust — outer core (liquid) — land — inner core (solid) — mantle

D2

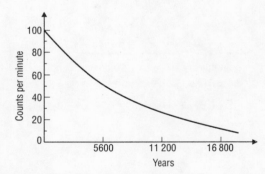

geostationary satellite

low orbit satellite

D6

clouds of hydrogen gas drawn together by gravity

nuclear fusion → helium and light energy

red giant

black hole · white dwarf · pulsar

E1 a) **unemployment**
b) **slag heaps, pollution of atmosphere when burned**
c) **non-renewable energy source, limited supply of coal.**

E2 **Advantages:** plentiful supply etc.
Disadvantages: supply seldom continuous etc.

E3

Energy input	Efficiency
chemical 2800 J	$1120/2800 \times 100 = 40\%$
electrical 1500 kJ	$1425/1500 \times 100 = 95\%$

E7 $t = E/ms$
$m = E/st$

E8 energy transferred = $2500 \times 60 \times 5$ joules in 5 minutes
mass of water $= E/ts = 2500 \times 60 \times 5/(10 \times 4200)$
$= 17.86$ kg

E9 Potential energy $= mgh$
$E = 0.5 \times 10 \times 0.5 = 2.5$ joules

E11 a) $E = mgh = 2.5 \times 10 \times 2 = 50$ joules
b) kinetic energy when hitting ground = potential energy lost = 50 joules
c) $v = \sqrt{(2gh)} = \sqrt{(2 \times 10 \times 1)} = \sqrt{20} = 4.4$ m/s

F1

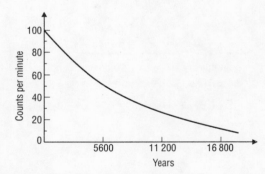

F2 c, g, e, f, b, a, i, d, h

F3 atomic number = 92, $\quad 2 + 90 = 92$
mass number = 238, $\quad 4 + 234 = 238$

Formation: ${}^{14}_{7}\text{N} + {}^{1}_{0}\text{n} \rightarrow {}^{14}_{6}\text{C} + {}^{1}_{1}\text{H}$
Decay: ${}^{14}_{6}\text{C} \rightarrow {}^{0}_{-1}\beta + {}^{14}_{7}\text{N}$